BEATING JOB

C000070700

DR DONALD SCOTT is Consultant in Clinical Neurophysiology at the London Hospital. He is the author of several books and over a hundred articles on neurophysiology, epilepsy and psychiatry. His books for a non-professional readership include *Coping with Suicide*, also published by Sheldon Press. Dr Scott lives with his wife, who is a psychologist, and two children in Blackheath.

To

Josie

with love

Donald

Mrs J. Scott
16, Main st
Kirriemuir

Overcoming Common Problems Series

Overcoming Common Problems Series

Overcoming Common Problems Series

Overcoming Common Problems

BEATING JOB BURNOUT

Dr Donald Scott

SHELDON PRESS
LONDON

First published in Great Britain 1989
Sheldon Press
SPCK
Marylebone Road
London NW1 4DU

British Library Cataloguing in Publication Data

Scott, Donald
    Beating job burnout. – (Overcoming common problems)
    1. Man. Stress. Self – treatment
    I. Title   II. Series
    158′.1

    ISBN 0–85969–597–2

Typeset by Deltatype Ltd, Ellesmere Port, Cheshire
Printed and bound in Great Britain by
Courier International Ltd, Tiptree, Essex

Contents

Acknowledgements

I wish to thank AMS for help in preparing and checking the manuscript, and Mrs Patricia Siddall for secretarial assistance.

1

Identifying the Problem

The alarm rings, you stir, struggle into consciousness. Thoughts of a pleasant weekend still linger – a birthday party with a trip to the theatre, perhaps – but you realize that you must go to work. Your job has been so dull lately, nothing happening, nothing new, the whole outlook totally uninspiring. Should you turn over in bed and forget it? This pattern is so often repeated. Everyone has experienced it at some time.

Even on your way to work the feeling of dullness and lack of interest remains, refusing to be pushed aside completely, but overcome mainly by a realization that one must go to work. On the other hand, perhaps, there may be a pain in the chest, the beginning of a cold or flu, real or imagined, to divert one from the commuter train to the doctor's surgery.

Is this all just a passing phase or the beginning of job stress and burnout? This condition is serious not only for the individual but for the economic health of the country as a whole; in fact it is a more important cause of time lost at work than physical illness.

Job burnout: what is it?

Burnout is a condition where a person has exhausted his/her capabilities in their job or field – be it factory, office, hospital or university. He/she can no longer function efficiently and feels under pressure at the thought of work, let alone in the workplace itself. Stress plays an important part in this disorder, which is not new but has become recognized recently in this form.

Mere staleness is a part, but more than that work becomes a total drudge. There are bodily ailments too which, often after long and thorough investigation, appear to have no serious underlying basis. Psychological features may also be prominent with panic attacks when approaching the office door, and

1

feelings of unsteadiness or unreality; difficulty travelling whether by car, train or underground are also common complaints.

Many different factors may cause stress of course, but in this book we shall concentrate on difficulties at work. These cannot be seen in isolation – problems at work may loom so large that they cause real difficulty in family or leisure settings. Advice and help can resolve some individuals' troubles, but others need counselling and professional assistance to overcome the difficulties. Burnout is not a trivial matter. It produces much more unhappiness than physical ailments or obvious psychiatric disorders. These, of course, do play a part – severe depressive illness obviously interferes with work.

Who suffers from job burnout?

Problems at work may happen to anyone and in any country; no-one is immune. Teachers in the United Kingdom have been in the press recently as having real difficulties because of stress due to classroom violence. Doctors also suffer, not least because the national health service is under pressure from underfinancing and perennial waiting list problems. Housewives, without a strict pattern, frequently find it difficult to keep going. So job burnout is an almost universal problem. The point can be argued that it is worse than it was 50 years ago, but this does not help the sufferer. The following case history may give an idea of how to cope with some of the problems.

Case history: Andrew

Andrew, 55, had been employed in the same firm all his life. He was conscientious, careful, hard-working and above all happy and contented. He had progressed steadily and unobtrusively over the years. The office staff under him were satisfied with his supervision. But during the course of his work life he had made few friends. Workmates regarded him as acceptable and pleasant but a little standoffish. They thought he considered himself superior.

At the same time as Andrew joined the firm as a school

leaver from the grammar school so did Mike. They worked alongside each other but in different offices with little contact, and though they had a friendship, it was never close. Andrew was devoted to his wife and two teenage daughters but was never very affectionate; he was also very quiet and distant, rarely going out or even speaking to the neighbours. He helped his wife with the garden but his hobby was stamp-collecting, which suited his perfectionist personality.

Very few problems arose until suddenly there was a takeover and reorganization of the group. Mike and Andrew both applied for promotion, but Mike was put in charge of that part of the firm where Andrew was employed. The picture changed. At first his wife could not really understand what had happened, but then she realized that something was seriously wrong. Andrew was no longer punctual and conscientious, he took days off for no apparent reason, his desk was piled high with unanswered letters and unread memoranda. Interest in his work, his wife saw, had completely disappeared. He bottled up all the problems. He did not mow the lawn and his stamp collection gathered dust, though he himself still denied that there was anything wrong.

Andrew slept fitfully, showed no interest in food and lost almost a stone (6½ kg) in weight quite quickly. He complained of back pain. At work he was argumentative and critical of everything. He said the plans for future development were useless, and bored him. He seemed difficult, embittered and spiteful. His friendship with Mike evaporated. He had obviously reached a crisis at work. Why?

To understand we must consider, as in other examples later, what has gone wrong with life overall. In some circumstances trouble at work can be pushed into the background as home, family and hobbies produce satisfaction, so clearly we must examine the whole person.

The 24 hours we have is divided roughly into three: one-third work, one-third sleep, and a third for chores and leisure. All three segments must 'work together'. If, for example, sleep is disturbed, home life and work will suffer. The three parts are quite closely interrelated and trouble in one may be reflected in another.

Andrew, then, had been passed over and lost his self-esteem, making him bitter and upset. What happened then was unfortunate. His new boss in charge of the whole group had heard from Mike and others of Andrew's irritability and upsetting behaviour, and called him for interview. He suggested that Andrew and his wife go on a cruise to have a break from problems at work. He wrongly thought that this would solve everything. However, this is just too simple a view and, though it seems a good idea, in practice most situations are not so straightforward, and 'getting away from it all' does not always provide a magic cure.

This proved to be the case for Andrew. He returned to work more irritable, difficult and argumentative than before. His timekeeping and incompetence led inevitably to the sack. When he went to his family doctor complaining now of severe backache, the latter recognized the signs of a severe depressive illness. Referral to a psychiatrist resulted, and treatment with antidepressants helped the worst symptoms, but then began the period of exploring the difficulties at work and how they had arisen.

After some months Andrew got another post, and returned to his efficient pattern of work with good timekeeping. His pride and self-esteem returned, he took an interest again in wife, family and hobbies. Other outcomes might have been less happy, for example resorting to drugs and alcohol or even suicide, as we shall see later.

Andrew had a very serious problem which required professional help. Not all job stress and burnout is so bad, and it can often be overcome by a simpler approach. But there is much we can learn from Andrew's story.

First and foremost he failed, unlike his wife, to recognize the problem. *Awareness* is the most important aspect as there is first aid action that can be taken (see page 28). In all cases the signs are a mixture of physical and mental – in Andrew's case, backache and irritability as well as inability to continue daily work or consider the future. Failure to obtain promotion or other disappointments are a common trigger for real problems at work. The new boss's 'magical cure' did not work, but the slow process of reorganization and rethinking did.

Health and work

Two other brief examples show the interplay between health in the wider sense and various areas of life including work.

First, take the sufferer from severe backache. Sometimes this develops on the basis of a serious physical disorder. At other times it is a nagging pain due to muscle spasm akin to tension headache. One of the main features, whatever the underlying cause, is a serious disturbance of sleep. Clearly this and the persistent pain will affect punctuality and concentration at work. Home life, social and sexual activity will also suffer. The condition may disappear with treatment, to recur at intervals later.

Second, take the partner who has an affair, particularly with someone in the same workplace. At first the change in the previously stable marital relationship may be almost imperceptible. But if discovered it may cause considerable strife. Because of various rivalries, poor decisions may be made concerning problems that naturally arise in the complex employment situation.

In these (and Andrew's) case action needs to be taken by someone – the person himself or herself, or perhaps the partner or someone close has to step in to prevent a worsening situation. Most important of all is for individuals to *see* job stress building up to burnout in themselves and others, and decide what to do.

First aid

On the job front, careful thought about what can be achieved in the short term as well as the long term is essential. Make a checklist of jobs to be done, and tick them off when completed. Each day something accomplished is part of the battle, and gradually terrible worries about the distant future will seem less bleak. Attention to personal health is essential. Exercise aids sleep and stimulates a healthy appetite. Cutting down on smoking, alcohol and coffee also help in the process, as well as sparing use of tranquillizers or sedatives.

Do less overtime at work, give more emphasis to family and friends, hobbies and leisure time. Cultivate interests out of work, so all energies are not devoted to the job. All this will frequently reduce the work stress, and problems there will not loom so large.

Sharing the worries with workmates, friends and family will help, but if this does not ease the difficulty, professional aid in the form of counselling may be the answer. We shall return to all these courses of action in more detail, especially in Chapters 4 and 5, and learn from other case histories how the problems were resolved.

Job burnout is important

Work difficulties impinge on almost all our lives. They must be recognized for what they are and careful thought is needed to resolve them. Later in the book we show how to recognize the earliest stages of job stress, before major burnout arises.

In Chapter 2 we examine just why we work and what leads to satisfaction or dissatisfaction with employment. Then we shall turn to recognizing a stressful situation, realizing that job burnout is a universal problem.

2
Why do we Work?

There are many reasons for working, one of the most obvious being, 'For the money'. This is clearly not the complete answer, because many people, for example, work for one of the worldwide voluntary agencies and receive virtually no financial reward. The very fact of having a job clearly provides something that we all need and find satisfying. Some choose jobs that produce less money than it is possible to obtain in other employment. Obviously the question does not have a straight-forward financial answer, as the example from someone in my hospital experience indicates.

Case history: Annette

Annette had worked as a medical secretary for more than 20 years, mostly in the same hospital and for one consultant. She typed, was quick and accurate with case summaries and outpatient letters, and she answered the telephone constantly. There were patients with urgent problems, perhaps demanding, angry or worried about their condition. Appointments had possibly gone astray. This and many other facets of hospital work – students to be taught and administrative burdens – produced problems with which Annette had to deal tactfully. She could have obtained twice as much in the business world. Suddenly she departed to take up just that option. Yet within a month she was back in hospital work.

The reason for leaving and returning is of great interest. A decision had been made to reorganize the secretarial services with a view to creating a new administrative post which would carry a considerably increased salary. In spite of Annette's years of devoted service and great experience, she failed to get this promotion. The loss of status – she was to be supervised by someone she regarded as much less qualified – triggered her departure. The new business post, however, carried none of the responsibilities Annette had had and enjoyed in her hospital work, so she returned there to a considerable decrease in take-home pay.

Job satisfaction

Status and self-esteem are important, and are often just as much or even more a reward as money. Loyalty to the employer, whether individual or organization, is one aspect that seems to have been totally lost in the current craze for permanent temporary secretaries, encouraged by money-grabbing agencies that have bloomed in the last few years. The ingredients are not loyalty, but good wages and freedom, at the expense of comradeship and all other aspects that a stable work relationship provides.

Work and its problems often cement these friendships so that they may develop on both a social and sexual level, sometimes leading to marriage. They may spring from clubs or relate to sporting activities provided by large organizations.

Health considerations often play a part. For example, the medical department will not only deal with injury at work and safety considerations, but many now devote time to preventing illness in the widest context. Provision of private medical insurance is frequently one of the perks of employees across the board.

Most important of all is the fact that employment within an organization, producing either goods or services, adds to our pride and wellbeing and helps us to continue functioning normally in both body and mind. We respond, therefore, to the carrot offered rather than the proverbial stick to drive us on.

Doctors: a special case

Those outside the medical profession often wish they had a job, a calling, a vocation that would offer ultimate satisfaction. There is the caring aspect for those who are sick and dying, job security, and though remuneration may not be good compared with that of a business executive, it is now reasonable at most levels. Yet a survey done in 1987 by Isobel Allen for the Policy Studies Institute showed some surprising findings. Half the young doctors, particularly the women, regretted their decision to take up a medical career. Women felt that though they had made a commitment to medicine in certain branches, such as surgery, they were not welcome. They reported the whole system as being geared to the full-time consultant, with little thought given to such matters as marriage and family life.

This dissatisfaction in the profession is because of the long hours of work, which result in fatigue and exhaustion that prevent the standard of care the young doctor wishes to deliver. Also, just when he or she is working hardest in the wards and operating theatres it is necessary to study for higher qualifications in order to climb the next rung of the ladder. Otherwise the attempts to reach the top of the pile – to become a hospital consultant, for example – will fail. There are also arguments about the personal patronage which operates – the 'old boy network' – reinforced by, for example, loyalty to a particular college or hospital in which the person trained.

Doctors at least have access to medical treatment for themselves and their families if illness occurs. Indeed health at work is of great importance outside as well as inside the medical profession. This has been underlined by employers providing health care in the private sector fairly frequently nowadays as well as a wide range of facilities on the work site.

Expert views

The famous psychiatrist Sigmund Freud commented that work provided the most important foothold for the maintenance of reality. Work really enables us to keep our feet firmly on the ground, and to interact with people. The discipline of timekeeping and direction of energy prevent us from drifting into a fantasy world.

Contrast the factory worker and the budding pop star. The former knows and perhaps detests the grind, looking forward desperately to Friday afternoon, but he has a time pattern, and a drive to finish the work. The pop star, on the other hand, dreams and drifts, using drugs and alcohol to fan his belief that a number one disc in the hit parade is just around the corner. He is living on fantasy rather than reality, which often leads to the problems we read about daily in the papers, underlining the importance of Freud's perhaps old-fashioned-sounding view.

Another expert, Professor Langeveld, gives several factors that enable us to maintain a healthy mental attitude. High on the list he puts rewarding interpersonal relationships, which allow the development of a feeling of security so that problems and conflicts can be overcome whether they are encountered at home or in the workplace. The development of skills at a particular task, and taking responsibility, are just two important stages in the fostering of this maturity. Knowledge of what we can do successfully and what we inevitably fail at is valuable, as it gives a clue as to how we organize our lives in the future, as well as what new avenues to follow. We must not, however, be overconfident; a realistic view of oneself is essential. This emerges particularly from the following case history.

Case history: Michael

Michael was an energetic young man who left school with a handful of good qualifications essentially in English language and literature. He had run the school magazine, in fact revived it from near death to a lively publication sought by parents, teachers and schoolmates alike. When he left school a job on a local paper was an answer to his journalistic flair. Within a year or two he had moved to a national paper, soon ascending the ladder, but Michael was trapped by what has been called the 'Peter principle' (put forward by a Canadian professor of the same name). The idea is that we are always promoted to a level higher than we can really manage. This happened to Michael. The signs of stress set in: vague physical illness, poor sleep, tension with wife and problems with his young family. He made the wise decision that London was not for him. The editorship of a substantial regional daily was his choice, and he is now happy and functioning well.

Walking away from stress

As we shall see later one of the solutions to stress at work, the boredom and the burnout, is to quit, walk away and find something else. For a teenager it is important to choose the right level and topic for his/her career, and not to be browbeaten by parents into something else.

We all know of the father who wants his son to be a farmer, a professor or a stockbroker, to follow in his footsteps, but attempting something at an inappropriately high level courts disaster. On the other hand there is the successful actor mother who takes the reverse attitude, almost obstructing her daughter's chosen career to follow her mother's role.

Case history: Jon

Bob exemplifies the problem. As the son of a professor of surgery he was encouraged to study medicine, although neither intellectually nor emotionally equipped for the work. He failed even his first year at university with great loss of face. Physiotherapy was the next step, but this was also a hard struggle with no success in his final exams. A period of lounging and loafing at home followed – then a decision. He successfully approached a local garage owner for a job – at once he was transformed into someone who dashed to work happily every day, rather than having to be forced out of bed to study. Now everyone buttonholes him to tune their sportscar; Jon has achieved self-reliance, one of the main aspects of maturity.

Finding the right niche allows us not only to fulfil ourselves, but also to develop so that we can cope with the general stresses of life that we shall inevitably encounter, not least in the workplace.

Work relationships

Them and us

Work has always been a place that can breed anger, conflict, ill-feeling, hostility, and outbursts of temper. The close proximity of workmates may lead to companionship and friendship outside the factory, or office, but also the reverse, like frayed tempers and bad emotional responses.

This is true at any level – boardroom, office, or shopfloor. However, the problem particularly arises between the worker and the 'boss'. Whether he is the foreman or the top executive there has traditionally been the 'them' and 'us' feeling which has helped the growth of the trade unions and professional organizations in general.

The 'them' and 'us' view is overcome by many means but most of all by communication. Motivating the workforce and telling them where the company is going, is important. This leads to stability within the organization. Employees buying shares, often at a discount, is one way to achieve satisfaction about the firm, and this has recently become much more widely practised and acceptable. However, the vagaries of the Stock Exchange do not necessarily further stability, and this form of investment is not universally favoured by employees.

The boss

A study in 1988 showed that only half the workers in a survey said that they were consulted in matters which affected them. Less than half respected their superiors, and a third believed that their boss neither worked hard nor cared about the work force. The conclusion was that 'managers will need to work harder at providing a human touch'. An expert has put it neatly with the four Cs: the ideal manager of the future has to Combine, Cost-consciousness, with Creativity, and the most important ingredient of all, Caring.

In fact, recent developments have hindered rather than furthered relationships between the boss and the 'others'. With computers it is possible to keep an eye on the speed at which the employee works, how quickly he presses the keys of visual display units, the duration of coffee or toilet breaks, as well as how many private phone calls are made on the office phone. How much laxity there should be in such matters is of course not clear. On the whole allowing a little leeway is, in my view and that of others, a good idea. A call to arrange theatre tickets for a wife or husband's birthday treat may take a minute and a very small amount of money, but may play on the worker's mind if he or she is not allowed to make that vital contact. It may indeed eat into a whole day's profit for the employer.

Extreme pressure at work leads to absenteeism that may be disguised as illness. Then there are the age-old excuses for being away from work – burying grandmothers on the day of a big match is just one example! Clearly flexibility is appropriate. The employee is less likely to take liberties, particularly if the old-fashioned influences such as pride in work, loyalty and self-respect are strong.

There are, of course still tyrannical bosses. As Patricia King, the American writer, puts it, 'Never work for a jerk'. She tells the story of Miranda who had the sort of boss who wanted reports typed before he had dictated them! One dark winter night Miranda was driving home when a car sped up behind and overtook her, forcing her onto the pavement. Was this a plainclothes cop, a rapist or a mugger? No, believe it or not, it was her slavedriver. As she rolled down the window he called out his oft-repeated words, 'Take a letter, Miss Smith'.

The workplace

Temperature regulation and lighting are important for buildings. Quite how these interplay with the internal arrangements in terms of desks and office space is uncertain, but interestingly enough there are some buildings which have bad reputations for producing stress and illness, so much so that the concept of 'sick building syndrome' has emerged. 'Sick building syndrome' is far from being fully understood.

Attention should be concentrated on such matters as safety, where there is no divergence of opinion.

A building site or coalmine have inbuilt risks not present in the office, but accidents can happen anywhere. However, they can be minimized by appropriate safety practices and this is especially important when the lives of others depend on them. A fire in a hotel, or an air crash, highlight the problem. Yet for the individual loyalty to the organization and caring will depend, not just on the perks, safety and attention to health needs, but on many other less obvious matters. The four Ds are not a bad summary: *D*esire, *D*etermination, *D*iscipline and *D*iligence. These and other items add up to satisfaction at work, shown in Table 1. You can easily add some more to reflect your own situation.

Table 1   Checklist: is your work satisfying?

- Do you feel you are in the right job, post or career?
- Is the pay, wage or salary reasonable?
- Apart from the money, is the work rewarding?
- Is it worthwhile mentally?
- Do you feel a personal commitment to the work, the firm, the boss?
- Is management conscious of your needs?
- Are the work conditions satisfactory, heating, rest space, toilets etc?
- Are there adequate safety precautions?
- Do you have any financial investment in your firm or organization?
- Would retirement, either early or at the usual age, come as a blow?
- Are there any worries about redundancies or takeovers?
- Are absentee rates low?
- Is there shift work or are there antisocial hours?
- Is the turnover of workers low?
- Is the employer concerned about your health, providing for example, medical facilities, private insurance etc?
- Are labour relations good?
- Have you thought about your work in this way before?

Look at Table 1 now, because it will help you to assess your own risk for job stress and burnout. It should be emphasized that the position of a particular item is not important because this varies with different people, but the more questions you can answer with 'yes' the better. Incidentally it was designed more to set you thinking than to produce concrete answers so beloved by psychologists. Nevertheless it is awareness of these and other factors that could be a solution to stress at work in your case, and the recognition of it by those close to you.

This is the theme of Chapter 3.

3

Warning Signs of Stress
and Job Burnout

Work has changed over the centuries. It has shifted from the field to the factory, from hand to machine, from making a single article to multiple production, from a static manual process to a moving production line. In all this the worker has been dragged along rather than considered. Then earlier this century the experts began to look at work with a view to increasing production. Time and motion studies were introduced, in some firms coupled with the expansion of ideas present much earlier in the philanthropists' manufacturing companies, such as Rowntrees, where the part played by the workers was carefully considered. He or she could be viewed as a person, rather than an automaton linked to the incessantly moving production belt, someone with no clear idea about the end product or its purpose.

However, only in the last ten years has attention focused on stress in the workplace, and now at least attempts are being made to help sufferers.

Almost anyone may experience stress, sometimes short-lived but at other times long-lasting. The dedicated, enthusiastic and idealistic are even more likely to be at risk than those who are more relaxed about their jobs and have other outlets for their energies, which tend to offset troubles, setbacks, and problems at work. These individuals are more able to resolve their difficulties and cope.

What causes stress?

The effects of stress are baffling and may be difficult to recognize. On one level it is simply part of the primitive body response to danger and conflict – fight or flight. The flight mechanism is inbuilt in all humans to deal with the fear present from the days of the caveman when tackling a big bear, to us when coping with the big boss. The body secretes chemical substances, the best known of which is adrenalin. This sets the heart pounding and causes a host of other changes including nervousness. If the fear is prolonged and 'spread out thinly' as one expert puts it, anxiety and stress result. There is overreaction – even the ring of an office telephone bell causes a startled response; so as you reach for the phone you think of strangling the person on the other end, rather than greeting them in the usual approved telephone manner.

It is, of course, true that a degree of tension is necessary for satisfactory work. The expression 'living on one's nerves' is a recognition of this fact, but it can get out of hand. Psychologists have a phrase for it, based on the names of two Harvard university professors, called the 'Yerkes–Dodson law' of job performance. In a nutshell, stress stimulates productivity but only up to a point – after that crucial point is passed a rapid decline in output results. The bodily physiological mechanisms – for example, adrenalin production – exceed normal levels, leading to unpleasant lasting symptoms. Those who live on their nerves, as one expert put it, tread a fine line between 'doing a great job' and being 'nervous wrecks'. The following is an example.

Case history: Wayne

Wayne was a successful supervisor for many years in a major motor manufacturing plant. Then the company was taken over and his career plummeted – his job became merely to buy supplies of paper and pencils! Wayne found that the orders were stacking up, not despatched to the suppliers. He tried to appease the angry secretaries for non-delivery and cope with the backlog by working long hours. His diligence was rewarded by the supervisor's hint that his job was being phased out anyway and he would be made redundant. Any risk of imminent unemployment is one of the sure foundations for severe job stress. Wayne had already suffered the upsetting effects of a takeover, another example of the instability behind many cases of serious work problems. So Wayne was now at a point where he was in acute danger of job stress and burnout.

He lost 2 stones (12½ kg) in weight, turned to drink and tranquillizers. He became mentally disturbed to breakdown point. The pressure mounted relentlessly until one day he entered the office with a gun.

Wayne was disarmed before he could hurt anyone, but he had lost his career, wife, family and house.

Reasons for job stress

As we have seen in Wayne's case, uncertainty in the workplace – takeover battles and redundancy threats – is one of the causes. Middle management often bear the brunt of stress, being under pressure from both shopfloor and boardroom. It is not so much the level in the pecking order, but the fact that at the very top of an organization there is more likelihood that the person can take effective action. It is those not able to extricate themselves from a difficult situation by actions who suffer. Like being trapped in a lift between floors, we have to wait for the engineer while tension rises. If there is a long delay, we may start kicking the sides of the lift to relieve tension.

Control of the situation is more important than danger. Take for example a racing driver: it is not speeding at 200 miles (320 km) an hour that causes tension, but the pit stop, where he sits in the car helpless, while the crew work at their speed changing tyres and carrying out repairs.

We have already seen that some situations are more likely to cause stress than others and if the problems are not resolved burnout results. In Table 1 we saw that there are many different aspects to job satisfaction.

Stress and particular jobs

Some jobs, however, present particular difficulties (Table 2). *Teachers* and head teachers nowadays have to combat classroom violence. They are not only severely stressed but they burn out early and leave the profession. Poor pay is another, but probably less important factor in the equation. *Junior doctors* are also under tension. They cannot control the number of patients who will become ill on the days when they are on rota to receive emergencies. Through the haze of fatigue and lack of sleep, they must somehow cope with whoever comes from the emergency room. *Journalists* are at risk, because of big boss editors and tight deadlines; so too are *air traffic controllers* who are pressurized partly because their performance on the job controls the lives and safety of many others, and partly by news stories of how many near misses there are.

Table 2   Examples of tough jobs (in alphabetical order)

- Air traffic contollers
- Customers' complaints department staff
- Journalists
- Junior hospital doctors
- Miners
- Oil-rig workers
- Police officers
- School teachers
- Secretaries
- Waitresses

At a different level the *waitress* is at the beck and call of diners, particularly when kitchen staff are inefficient or incompetent. The *complaints department* of a store is another example where workload is unevenly distributed between a quiet Monday morning and the Saturday afternoon crush. *Secretaries* too – we have already heard the story of Miranda and her tyrannical boss – may snap when suddenly presented with a thirty-page manuscript to be typed up 'urgently' just as they were preparing to go home after a particularly demanding day at work.

Dangerous work

Danger is another factor that most of us do not have to consider in relation to employment. We probably pay lip service to fire drill and emergency exits and that is it. However, for some there is a real and ever-present danger of serious injury and possible death. Consider an offshore *oil worker* in the North Sea or off the Alaskan coast. He lives and works on a time bomb. Experts who studied oil riggers found that 30 per cent have been involved in an accident causing personal injury. Interestingly, those at risk were the very ones who found their employment most anxiety-provoking. They were dissatisfied with their lot in many respects including lack of privacy or leisure facilities. Problems at home were caused by the work pattern with perhaps alternate weeks at work and on shore. Wages were high but the price paid in human terms – the risk of very serious accidents – was great.

Miners and *policemen/women* also face ever-present physical danger. And they see harrowing sights, the dead and maimed in road or other accidents, as do *ambulancemen* and *firemen*. Sometimes the images of horrendous events do not recede quickly. The *underground train* or *bus drivers* who are involved when there is a suicide attempt or an act of hooliganism, or are spat on by passengers because of breakdown and subsequent delay, are also stressed and desperate to escape to the safety of their homes.

Firemen and other public servants are particularly exposed to tragedy, as seen in the following case history.

Case history: George

George, a fireman, was called out to a road accident, a head-on motor crash with mother and seven-year-old daughter lying critically injured, and the father still trapped behind the steering wheel. Within minutes he was lifeless and the other two died within two days.

The vivid image of this carnage was present all day long and coloured George's dreams. He slept badly and ate poorly. He cried like a child, at first all the time, and then later whenever he saw anything about death or accidents on television. It is surprising how much of even news bulletins show scenes of violence, injury and suffering of all kinds. He, like so many involved in major disasters, only recovered with counselling. Time, though it usually heals eventually, is very slow.

Predicting work stress and burnout

When dealing with human behaviour and activity it is most important to be able to predict what might happen in a certain situation. We know about the 'tough jobs' (see Table 2), but it is the individual who matters.

Let us examine the *politician* and his risks. Difficulties are present in many countries all over the world. In the UK parliament, he may be in opposition or a backbencher. As one main factor in job stress is lack of stability, the member of parliament, who is dependent on the next general election result, is at risk. Can his wishes be translated into action or not? In the factory situation the boss is able to do so but the shop floor worker is not. Transferring this to the parliamentary situation we see that the Prime Minister is in the best position; there is greater stress, but action is possible. So, depending on the rank of the particular politician in the governing party, this pattern also applies to a greater or a lesser extent.

The Leader of the Opposition is in an unenviable situation.

Table 3 Some warning signs of job stress

- Headache, noises in the ear, dizzy spells
- Vague ill-health, poor appetite and weight loss
- Stomach ache and diarrhoea
- Palpitations, chest pain
- Nervous tics, nail-biting and scratching
- Sleeplessness and bad dreams
- Irritability and depression
- Fatigue and restlessness
- Poor memory and concentration
- Increased smoking, use of alcohol and tranquillizers

When a difficulty has arisen on, for example, a controversial foreign policy issue, he is pressed strongly to resolve not only this problem, but conflicts between the various wings of the Party. As his stress level rises, talk of resignation is in the air. Clearly, as stress in this situation is difficult to resolve burnout and consequent resignation may be inevitable.

Warning signs

It is crucial to *recognize* the warning signs of stress: the individual often does not see them, and it falls to spouse, family members or workmates to realize what is happening. If the signs are mainly physical (Table 3) the general practitioner may be able to spot them. There is vague general ill-health, with stomach pains, bowel upsets, loss of interest in food but desire for sweets and chocolate, backache and muscle pains. Headache, noises in the head, dizzy spells and unsteadiness are other signs of trouble. The following case history shows what might happen.

Case history: Albert

Albert, a 47-year-old council road sweeper, was seen in the casualty department of the local hospital following dizzy spells. These had occurred at work, and similar attacks had happened in the past over a period of a few years, increasing more recently. He described an unsteady feeling in his head and butterflies in his stomach. His legs felt heavy as though they would give way. He did not fall but had to sit on the kerb until the feelings passed, which often took up to half an hour. At home Albert was irritable and demanding. At work he complained of being constantly tired, and though he slept badly he would also take a daytime nap, perhaps extending to much longer in the evening when he got home. Night sleep was broken by frightening dreams from which he would wake in a cold sweat with his heart beating rapidly. Investigations failed to show any physical cause for the symptoms which worsened. Headaches and panics with palpitations, and unsteadiness while walking became more and more of a problem. He was frequently away from work and no medication or any other treatment suggested by the hospital doctor or his general practitioner were of any use. Absence from work led to his redundancy, and his anxieties about wife and family became more marked, coupled with his own symptoms. As a result he was unable to return to any useful employment whatsoever.

In Albert's case there seemed no particular reason for his difficulties until it became clear that a new supervisor and, later, privatization of council work had led to considerable pressure. He was unable to adapt: a clear case of job burnout.

Stress symptoms

Fatigue coupled with poor sleep and bad dreams (as in Albert's case) are quite common features. There may be pains in the chest, and concern about heart attacks. Psychologically, lack of concentration and inability to finish tasks as well as mental lapses such as forgetting birthdays and anniversaries are common. Nail-biting and scratching may be obvious in some. Inability to sit still in the chair and read a newspaper, watch television or pursue hobbies are all features. Sometimes the person develops quite severe depressive symptoms with feelings of unworthiness and loss of interest in everything, as shown in the case history below.

Case history: Stephen

Stephen was 32 when he first became depressed. His work as a salesman for an electrical goods firm had occupied him satisfactorily for several years. His good work record and the retirement of the branch manager made him an obvious choice for successor. But he found the burden of administrative work irksome and he became obsessed with details about stock level. He found supervising younger, inexperienced and casual salesmen difficult. From being a cheerful, outgoing person who made every effort to satisfy customers and staff, he became not only irritable but also totally disinterested in

23

the work that had previously given him pleasure. He was a regular attender at the local football club and played snooker fairly frequently, but these no longer appealed. His doctor fortunately realized the depressive nature of his symptoms which were relieved by medication.

The illness, depression in Stephen's case, was not just a minor feeling of sadness but a serious condition often with many bodily symptoms which had a tendency to recur on occasion and required electroconvulsive shock treatment. Clearly the complaints from which he suffered could well have been interpreted entirely as job burnout. In fact this was not really the case. However, this illness may run in families, and in any case may recur again and again in the individual, so partners must be on the lookout for warning signs.

Overwork

Overwork can be the response to demands of the firm or organization, a sign of impending job burnout. Trying to make up for inefficiency with long hours, or attempts to increase take-home pay, are sometimes given as reasons; just a quirk of personality that leads to a person being labelled a 'workaholic' is one possible explanation. Many studies by experts have shown that overwork, for whatever reason, is characteristic of those who develop heart attacks: overwork plus stress equals heart attack. The professionals define a particular type of personality they have called type A; the profile is a typical union-bashing senior executive who is a hard driver and relentless achiever. Interestingly, these very individuals have their routines for fitness and exercise as well as weight control, but the stress of overwork counteracts all the profit these activities might bring – they are no longer relaxing or beneficial.

Take, for example, the top executive on a major TV channel. He sacked the cameraman and then worked a non-stop 12 hour day from 3.0 am, supervising secretaries while they held the cameras. This kind of person is highly competitive, aggressive, very conscious that time is passing by, time in which results could be achieved. Not surprisingly hobbies and recreations are few and far between in this individual's Filofax. Leisure is not relaxation, it is thirty lengths of the pool in half an hour, or squash three times a week.

The actual mechanism by which this type of activity leads to a heart attack is not clear, but constant surges of adrenalin stimulating the heart to rapid and intensive beating is obviously a factor. The walls of the arteries that feed the heart with oxygen and other necessary substances for activity of the muscle become strained and damaged, so a clot may form. Severe chest pains are a sign that all is not well. The body of a living organism is not a machine: type A personalities are in most danger of wearing themselves out.

Life events

Apart from personality considerations, other factors lead to illness. We are probably already familiar with some of them from our own experience: the death of a partner or a family member, divorce and separation, and even pregnancy seem to predispose to ill-health. Not surprisingly, having a serious accident or a scrape with the law leading to a court appearance, particularly if a jail sentence results, may again produce effects on health and wellbeing. Financial problems, even taking out a large mortgage, also figure. Experts have shown that some life events are more important than others. Dismissal, retirement, change in business or even in job, or friction with the boss, not to mention increased work responsibility or alteration in working patterns may lead to physical illness.

The condition may be severe – heart disease or a serious elevation in blood pressure – but minor ailments such as tension headaches and backaches may also occur as a result of these changes. These health problems may recur with subsequent life events. Take the case of the American seaman and the various problems that occurred over 20 years of his life.

Case history: Jackson

Jackson was 20 years old when he joined the Navy in 1941. He was aboard a ship in Pearl Harbor when the Japanese attacked. He was transferred to another ship, but unfortunately it was later torpedoed and sunk. He survived and tension headaches developed but later resolved. With two more changes of ship as well as promotion, tension symptoms returned but did not prove a major problem.

After the war, at 26, he married and soon developed backache. Then began a clustering of life events of the sort that can lead to illness. He was demobilized, but re-enlisted in the Navy and this was followed by two changes of ship and shore station. His first child was born and his wife was again pregnant. In the following year Jackson developed tonsillitis, gonorrhoea and injured both wrists and his knees.

The next eight years were relatively calm and marked only by two absences from duty with minor ailments. Then, at age 37 a calamitous series of happenings took place. His wife developed a severe depressive illness when he was at sea. He returned to find that she had moved, with all the household effects and $1000 from the saving account. Jackson found her in the nearby town living with another man but was unable to recoup his losses. One week later on board ship he suffered a severe electric shock in the galley and almost died. His recovery was prolonged with inability to speak which was probably of psychological origin rather than a direct effect of the electricity.

Jackson did recover fully, obtained a divorce and custody of the children; but these events had taken their toll. He developed a severe depressive reaction and was discharged from the Navy on the grounds of his disability. Tension symptoms, headache, backache and gastric problems were all prominent at this stage.

This case history shows how illness and life problems come together, a feature all of us have noted to a greater or lesser extent. Obviously difficulties cannot be foreseen but it is clearly important to be aware, if we have been exposed to any particular traumas both in relation to work or personal life, that this is a time when health problems may arise.

The importance of spotting early signs of stress cannot be overemphasized because simple actions can often be taken. These may not cure the problems, but they can reduce them and prevent major disasters arising. This is the subject of Chapter 4.

4

Taking Action

As soon as the first signs of stress at work appear action must be taken. The individual must recognize the problem. Recognition and acceptance is the key to a series of important steps to be taken. These are shown in Table 4.

Table 4   Ways to cope

- Plan, set priorities and make appropriate time scales
- Set realistic short-term, medium-term and long-term goals
- Make a list of jobs, check them off one by one as completed
- Do a simple task each day
- Resolve to develop and maintain good health
- Take ample but not too much sleep
- Eat a balanced diet, lose weight if necessary
- Take regular exercise
- Cut down on coffee, smoking, alcohol and tranquillizers
- Increase recreation; develop hobbies, take up a creative interest or do voluntary work
- Share problems with family, workmates and friends
- Seek professional help – medical, psychiatric, financial, legal – as appropriate
- Do not give up, attempt to reduce job stress, but quit if you must

---

The first step

First of all get a pad and pencil and, taking a deep breath, start making a list of chores to be done, problems that are worrying you. Lists are essential. They help put matters into perspective. You can often clear the memory of problems that are really worrying you if they are put down on paper. Single sheets (write on one side only) spread out on the desk or table and headed

28

appropriately are my preferred arrangement. Notebooks or personal organizers can be used later.

Step aside and examine the mess that you are in. But do not be too solemn, think of something funny if you can and maintain a sense of humour throughout – as the boss of a small independent radio station puts it, 'when the going gets really tough – crack a joke . . . inject an element of humour into the place especially when things get frantic'.

The time scale

I find it useful to consider the pile of chores to be demolished along a particular scale: very short-term, medium-term, and long-term. Separate work from domestic problems. Do not attempt to do too much on the first occasion, certainly at this planning stage; several sessions will be needed to get sorted out. I personally often take and complete a simple task, not necessarily the most important, as it is always good to achieve something. Psychologically, this is a method of reinforcement, and with the strength gained one can go on from there. Do not be distracted, complete each item as you reach it.

Starting with 'very short-term', consider what you must do today or tomorrow. Then tackle successfully the other short-term items for this week. Medium-term can be thought of as 'this month'. Sometimes putting long-term aims into perspective helps most of all because we see where we are really going.

At the preliminary sorting stage you may find that ideas seem to crowd into the head 'trying to get out'. At this stage get your spouse, partner or family to help in the sorting out, particularly with the long-term objectives.

Making a start

List-making in itself causes considerable relief, often because when problems are placed in a realistic time scale, they do not seem so overwhelming. Do not, however, expect too much change too quickly. We are dealing with problems that have usually been building up over weeks, months or even years, and resolution may follow the equivalent time scale.

Case history: myself

Let me give an example from my own experience which, though specific, is a general indication. I decide to write a book; it has been in the back of my mind for some time and I have collected material, but it is in a muddle. So out come the inevitable sheets of paper as I try to marshall the press clippings and the rough notes. The lists of books to be consulted must be put in some order. I grasp at a possible title, perhaps several, write them down, then make out a table of contents. The preface is important as it gives an idea of who the book is aimed at, then where to go?

In the short-term, read the rough notes; in the medium-term make a list of chapter headings, and notes under each as to what they will contain without any particular thought of the final form. As I do so perhaps another title springs to mind, or another group of possible readers to be added to the preface as a target population.

The long-term aim, of course, is to be published, but where? I have to consult experts and colleagues who may know something of the field. So a pattern gradually emerges, and as I get it into the theme and a kind of order begins to emerge, my enthusiasm increases. I have formed an overall plan and can see the finished article vaguely in the distance; I now know what my aims are for today, tomorrow and so on.

So I have begun and it has been almost painless, in fact I feel better already!

Tackle important matters first

Quite often my experience has been that important problems are a sticking point. If you cannot tackle them head on, perhaps some emotional 'block' is present and this is stopping you. If this is the case how can it be overcome? You can't decide? Then leave that and press on with something else, simple chores that you can do after you have listed the more crucial tasks. Oddly, sometimes if one actually starts on simple tasks, an idea about the more difficult ones darts into consciousness and the method of tackling that problem falls into place.

Nevertheless, the serious matters – financial, legal, health, marital or sexual – must be confronted, even without a flash of inspiration. You must seek help.

If money is the problem, simply write to or ring the bank manager, and make an appointment to see him. He may be more sympathetic than you think, then dealing with the matter will progress naturally so you do not need to worry about it any more at this stage. If it is a problem with the law you must get appropriate advice and help. With health concerns do not delay; if you are worried about something go to the doctor. A lump in the breast will not go away, but it may not be cancer – what a relief when you find this out. A pain in the chest may not be the forerunner of a heart attack, but clearing away these worries will give you energy to devote to the real problems that require attention. The situation is rarely as bleak as you think.

How do you spend your time?

It is important to make a note of how your time is spent. Sleep enough but not too much. Twelve hours in bed leads to sluggishness and depression at the start of the day; six hours may be quite enough. Couple this with breakfast and regular meals rather than constant snacks. Set aside time for exercise, a brisk walk before bed, or at the very least using stairs rather than a lift constantly will help. Cut down on smoking, coffee, alcohol and tranquillizers. All these may increase tension in various ways, and are examined in detail in Chapter 5. If you are overweight go on a long-term rather than a crash diet for effective reduction. Dispel any health worries; don't brood on them. Always, as I said above, contact professional advisors – doctor, bank manager, health visitor or priest. Plan to make one phone call or write one letter a day arranging to see them. Then cross these off your list. You have made another important preliminary move.

Too much overtime?

We have said that excessive overtime may lead to heart trouble and indeed other health problems. The financial rewards do not always make up for disruption of home and family life. Overtime is often inefficient – extra hours at the desk for someone already stale and tired are unproductive. Try and avoid overtime if possible, but if it is essential arrange to do the less arduous tasks like catching up on reading, planning ahead for the following week rather than compiling hefty memoranda. When the mind is relaxed the future can be seen more positively both at work and at home. One can see perspectives more clearly without being dogged by depressive emotions that cloud the day-to-day working week.

Recreation is literally re-creation. It must be developed, by making exercise fun, and expanding hobbies and creative interests. Some find that voluntary work is a great outlet whether it is helping in a local home, or a conservation project – something totally different from work in another place with other people and the possibility of new friends and new pursuits.

It is also essential to get time away from work, make use of long weekends and concentrate on short breaks rather than a big annual family holiday which may present problems of its own. Marital difficulties may then rear their ugly head, or worsen, in two weeks of 24 hour-a-day constant contact between partners and children.

How people cope: some examples

Let us now examine how various people have grappled with their stressful work situations.

Acting

A 40-year-old actor turned to yoga to cope with the enormous pressures of the profession, particularly auditioning, when absolute mastery is necessary, not only of the voice but posture, not to mention remembering the words. Yehudi Menuhin, the world-famous violinist, turned to meditation during a period of strain and this helped his violin playing, clearly a pursuit that demands very high standards of bodily control as well as intense mental agility.

Farming

Farming may seem to be a relaxed, tension-free occupation – not so. Remember that command of the situation is the essential factor in the release of tension, and for much of farming the weather is important, planting and harvesting being examples of when good conditions are needed which are certainly not under the farmer's control. A sharp storm lasting just half an hour may reduce the grain crop from high quantity human food to pig swill. Lambs are delicate creatures, and a snowfall can be disastrous to the newborn. There *are*, of course, compensations in country pursuits – walking, fishing and friendly chats on market days. Learning to mellow and relax is essential for survival. But nowadays the farming world is a ruthless one, where machines are very expensive and top quality products are demanded by the food processors; it is not an easy existence.

University life

A professor at the top of the pile seems safe enough if not invincible. But he also is vulnerable, particularly in relation to money. Carrying out research requires high salaries, to be won from government and grant-giving agencies, charitable or commercial, such as drug firms in the case of medicine. These grant applications are time-consuming to prepare, and it is frustrating when they are rejected. Even if the application is successful they may only extend over three or four years. A professor may find that riding a motor bike round country lanes rids him of stress, the exhilaration and the spice of danger concentrates the mind, and the Medical Research Council seems miles away.

Parliament

An MP's wife has a difficult life. She sees her husband under stress in the constituency and in Parliament. Will he get a government post? Will he regain or win his seat at the next election? She cannot help him directly but must be willing, loyal and supportive in the various ups and downs of politics. Every hour of the week ahead is organized. She has to pack the car for the trip from the constituency to Westminster, give the goldfish or hamster to the neighbours, take the dog to kennels. All the domestic trivia need attention, while her husband deals with the constituency surgeries and all the numerous reports and correspondence that parliamentary work entails. Music on tape in the car or live at home, gardening or tennis may help her unwind.

In this chapter I have dealt with the possible ways of tackling various forms of stress, concentrating on work, in simple, practical terms. These largely depend on organizing oneself and obtaining help from the immediate environment. In Chapter 9 I shall deal with how to obtain help from various sources.

5

Smoking, Alcohol and Drugs

This book is not designed to be a guide to better health, but just as work cannot be seen in isolation from home life so our state of health affects the way we react in all situations. It changes our attitudes and responses, both of which are greatly influenced by the substances we have at hand. These have been available from time immemorial and can, in moderation, smooth our path. Alcohol, coffee, tobacco and even tranquillizers have their place but a more in-depth look at their effects is useful at this point.

Table 5   Towards a more healthy lifestyle

- Eat less salt, sugar, starchy foods and fats, and more fruit and vegetables
- Combat overweight by dieting slowly
- Exercise little and often; consider walking, jogging and swimming
- Restrict caffeine-containing drinks – coffee, coke and tea
- Limit smoking, or stop altogether
- Control alcohol intake; keep a diary of how much you drink and the cost, obtain help to stop if there are signs of dependency
- Tranquillizers should be used sparingly; make attempts to withdraw
- Beware of 'street drugs'
- Concentrate on relief of stress at source

Magazines and newspaper articles provide a great deal to read on health matters so I shall only touch on the main points. These sources contain good advice as do many books. Table 5 gives a series of important signposts pointing in the right direction for our purpose. Good health makes us better able to cope with stress wherever it arises. In this chapter we deal with exercise and eating healthily, and avoiding tobacco, caffeine, alcohol and drugs.

Food

Concern and awareness of what we eat, and what foods actually contain, has increased greatly and quite rightly in recent years, paradoxically side by side with the growth of 'fast food'. Diet and weight loss methods occupy considerable space in magazines and newspapers in infinite variety.

There are however some simple rules to follow. For most people it is important to eat less, particularly of sugar, starchy foods, fats and meat, but increase fruit and vegetables which contain fibre, an important and now well-recognized constituent of the diet. Being overweight is not necessarily a problem, but it does make taking exercise more difficult, an important point in feeling positively healthy. Unnecessary weight tends to be linked with high blood pressure and resulting heart trouble and strokes. Also for this reason restriction of salt intake is important, bearing in mind that many processed and tinned foods, and items such as tomato ketchup and pickles, contain large quantities of salt. Some people take extra vitamins and minerals, which for most of us are unnecessary but will do no harm.

Exercise

Regular exercise has many beneficial effects. It burns up unwanted calories, but it is not very efficient – you can walk over a mile on an egg! But, more importantly, exercise has a relaxing effect. Work or other problems seem to fade when one is jogging or swimming. Indeed running has been prescribed by some doctors in the United States as a good treatment for chronic depression. There is a warm glow of satisfaction afterwards, whatever the exercise, and it aids sleep for those who have insomnia. For a non-athlete little and often is better than a hard game of squash or an intense fitness programme at the weekends.

Coffee

Caffeine-containing drinks such as coffee may seem harmless enough, but recently caffeine has been pinpointed as a cause of serious conditions such as heart disease. However, from the point of view of stress symptoms, all caffeine-containing drinks require attention – tea and coke are also important sources of this stimulant. In small doses it makes us more alert, but excess causes unpleasant feelings and aches in the stomach, pounding of the heart, headaches, tremulous hands, a feeling of agitation and jitteriness. In other words it mimics stress symptoms, so modest amounts of caffeine are suggested, if really necessary. Some feel better with decaffeinated coffee or fruit drinks.

Tobacco

Watch a person under stress. One cigarette is barely extinguished before the next is lit. Tobacco does have calming effects in small amounts, and to prove this all one needs to do is to cut down or stop altogether, when a host of withdrawal symptoms appear. The trouble is that like alcohol and other drugs more and more is required to produce the same effect and this carries serious health risks. Lung cancer is one, but other chest conditions and heart disease are more important in terms of numbers affected. Indeed some surgeons will not consider heart bypass surgery to circumvent a blocked vessel to the heart muscle unless the patient gives up smoking. Nicotine causes constriction of the very arteries that need to be wide open to let the maximum flow of blood get to the heart where it is urgently needed for the maintenance of life.

Smokers are more than twice as likely to drink heavily, and to the same extent they are also more likely to be unfit. In addition the experts found, perhaps more surprisingly, that they are more likely to be dissatisfied with their lives, prone to violent arguments and taking time off work, do not like seat belts, and are three times more likely to use tranquillizers or anti-depressants.

Alcohol

Drinking alcoholic beverages is almost as old as man himself; they are consumed in all parts of the globe and are increasing worldwide, so why do they need consideration in relation to work?

First of all, alcohol is used by many as a tranquillizer, it is relatively cheap and has remained so in this country proportionate to the rapid rise in incomes over the last 20 years. In fact the price of spirits in real terms has actually fallen progressively over a period of years even taking inflation into account. Alcohol consumption tends to increase just when work or other stress is rising, and this makes matters worse because coping becomes even more difficult. True addiction to alcohol can come about without the individual even being aware of it. The line that divides social from addictive drinking is faint.

So what are the effects of alcohol? It acts as a stimulant; with small amounts, voices become louder and speech quicker, the jokes become funnier and bluer. It takes the lid off our natural reserve and we become more sociable. Even a relatively modest intake may lead to problems; most of us have known the embarrassment of the day after an office party. Alcohol clouds the memory, and greater and more continuous amounts may produce long gaps in memory.

Alcohol taken to relieve stress, as distinct from socially, actually has the opposite effect, because in larger amounts, it is both toxic and strongly depressant. Not infrequently newspapers report a death after a stag party, for instance, when someone was stupidly persuaded to down a bottle of gin in one.

The trouble with using alcohol to reduce stress, which it may at first appear to do, is that it reinforces the habit and more and more needs to be consumed. It also costs money, leading to squabbles at home with partners and family. The sportsman loses his prowess. Boasting at the bar and extravagant spending are coupled with inefficiency at work, not to mention accidents on the road, in the factory and at home.

There are some general rules to prevent a serious habit

forming. Drinking every day should be avoided, particularly at lunchtime, and of course before work in the morning, if used to dispel a hangover. Limit the total number of units taken in the week, half as many for women as for men. A unit is half a pint of beer, a glass of wine or a pub measure of spirits. A maximum of 21 units a week is allowed for men, but there must be two or three days without drinking, and women are allowed only a total of 14 units a week with the same proviso. This sort of level of alcohol consumption has been recommended by professionals in the field and was thought to be quite safe, but even that is probably risky both physically and psychologically, at least for those of the population who cannot maintain drinking within these bounds. It is also very dangerous to the unborn baby.

Doctors not averse to a drink sometimes find it difficult to have a clear view of the matter; indeed the cynic has suggested that an alcoholic should be defined as 'one who drinks more than his doctor'. If you feel that you have a problem keep a strictly honest diary showing just how much you are drinking and indeed spending on alcohol. You may get a surprise! Alcohol is so much a feature of life, both socially and from the shopfloor to the boardroom that control may be difficult. The construction worker's liquid lunch or the businessman's three-course feast to cement a deal for the director, may result, even with moderately modest alcohol intake, in an accident on the building site or a car crash on the way back to the office.

Doctors have come to recognize these problems in the emergency department as well as the wards of their hospitals, where blame for anything from indigestion to high blood pressure can be laid at the door of overindulgence. With the advent of easier and cheaper computerized blood screening methods it is quite simple to identify those who are drinking too much, even if they are not truly alcoholic. We can use the CAGE questions. C stands for Control: 'have you attempted to Control and Cut down your drinking?' A is for Annoyed: 'when asked, do criticisms about your alcoholic consumption upset you?' G concerns Guilt about drinking; and E for 'Eye openers', early morning drinks. The following examples show how two people dealt with drink problems.

Case history: Dr Ewing

Dr Ewing, 45, was a general practitioner who qualified in a famous Scottish medical school. There he learnt not only about medicine but about drinking. This started him on his habit which continued for many years until his partner persuaded him that he was out of control and should seek help.

Dr Ewing did so, not really because he considered that it was required, but because his partner threatened to report his behaviour while intoxicated. Dr Ewing was a careful, conscientious person whom the patients adored, but he found the work stressful, not least because he also had to look after an ill wife who was chairbound with multiple sclerosis.

It was partly due to this pressure that his drinking had accelerated and made him less able to cope with his children who were even more demanding because of their mother's incapacity. Judgement at work became quite clouded, and at home problems piled up. Dr Ewing apparently could not decide, or indeed care, how he would extricate himself, so the referral impressed on him by his partner proved to be just what was needed. He became totally abstinent, reorganized his home with outside assistance, got the children to lend a hand, and brought in a nurse to the practice to help with work that Dr Ewing had often done himself.

With this the picture changed. There were occasional lapses, but twelve years on Dr Ewing was fit and coping. Even when his wife became bedridden and finally died he did not feel a compulsion to return to the bottle.

Case history: Julian

Julian was about the same age as Dr Ewing, and in some ways there were similarities. He worked in the wine trade, and was extremely hard-working and conscientious. Social and business drinks were commonplace but in the early days Julian did not attend all the functions and would return home to his wife.

He had always been careful about drinking at lunchtime,

but this gradually started and within five years he had run into serious trouble. In those years he insisted that entertaining clients at lunch was an essential part of the business. He began to drink spirits as he bought a round of drinks for his group. In a relatively short period he started going to the pub at opening time before lunch and continued drinking until evening closing time. Though the employers provided some expense money for Julian's entertaining, this did not cover his costs and he reacted by increasing his expense account claims when he was not involved in business deals. This deception was inadequate to meet the bills, and in due course he retained money from clients rather than passing it on to his employers. The accountant quickly picked up the discrepancy, and Julian was admitted to hospital for treatment. Unfortunately his outcome was not successful and within a few years he had died of cirrhosis of the liver.

Julian was in one of the trades where addiction to alcohol is a real problem, partly because of ready access, but also because those who have developed the drinking habit, even if not actually alcoholics at that stage, do just such jobs. Stressful work also shows greater than average alcohol-related problems. Journalists, doctors and judges are all at risk but no-one is immune – and who would have expected to find football players in this category with such an emphasis on fitness. Good physical stamina is badly impaired by alcohol, yet we often read in the papers of sportsmen who have been in drunken brawls or have been stopped by the police, breathalysed and found to be over the limit. The rule put forward some years ago by an expert is helpful, particularly in relation to stress, *never drink when you feel you need one*.

Tranquillizers

With tranquillizers and alcohol there is a tendency for experts to use the word 'dependency' rather than 'addiction'. In the case of drugs, whether prescribed or so-called 'street drugs' (see below), there is both the strong desire and need to increase the dose in order to maintain the effect. The mental and physical aspects of dependency are revealed once the drug is stopped, causing symptoms varying from the unpleasant to the very serious. Doctor-prescribed drugs have increased in number and variety over the past 30 years. There is a pill for every need – to calm, to excite, to stimulate, to put to sleep, alert, even cure when we are vomiting. Some may make us sick when we do not want to be, but, most important, some make us well when we are ill. All, however, may produce side-effects that no-one wants.

Tranquillizers really do work on a short-term basis, and help deal with anxiety arising after an accident or a bereavement. It is their random prescription and long-term use that causes problems. The benzodiazepine family, consisting of lorazepam (Ativan), diazepam (Valium), nitrazepam (Mogadon), chlordiazepoxide (Librium) and many others, are very effective; for that reason they can be dangerous because of the tendency to increase the dose to maintain a particular desired effect. They also cause sleepiness, an effect boosted by alcoholic drinks making a particularly dangerous combination when skilled tasks such as driving are involved.

There is also a rebound aspect. This means that when the drug wears off the symptoms for which it was prescribed return with even greater impact and therefore lead naturally to an increased intake. Also after years of use it is very difficult to wean some people off the drug. Doctors have recognized the real problems and are now taking effective action; there are also various groups of ex-tranquillizer users who have provided help for those who wish to curtail their use of these drugs and are finding it difficult. However, as it is vital that the dose is reduced *very* gradually the length of time until the drug is completely stopped is often months and years depending on the total daily dose. In most cases both medical and social support are essential.

Case history: Philip

Philip, 42, had real problems. His car business was doing badly and he was a fairly heavy pub drinker. He increased his intake, and then his difficulties began. He could not cope with his

business which was sold for a pittance. His general practitioner had not appreciated Philip's alcohol intake, because
the patient had, as is common, only told half the truth. His
symptoms were of severe anxiety, tremulousness and difficulty with sleeping. Tranquillizers were the obvious solution.
Philip managed to persuade the doctor to prescribe more and
more but also bought some from a 'bent' pharmacist. His
intake was three or four times the usual dose and he was still
very tense within an hour of taking the tablets. However, he
found that by careful supervision and substituting a non-
addictive antidepressant he could reduce the dose by a quarter
of a tablet every fortnight – but in the end he needed hospital
treatment for detoxification. This uncovered many problems
between himself and his wife. With intense psychiatric help
some resolution was possible, but his severe family difficulties
were reinforced by a teenage son's suicide attempt. However,
Philip is now off tranquillizers, and indeed all drugs, although
he still finds difficulty returning to work.

Clearly tranquillizers and alcohol may help initially – but they are
really best avoided totally if there is a stress factor. Attention
should be focused on reducing this rather than masking it.

Street drugs

So much has been written about illicit drugs that more than a
brief mention here would be inappropriate. All can lead to
dependence of varying degrees of seriousness. Heroin carries a
particular risk because of physical problems, infections from
needles including AIDS, and severe craving. While cannabis is
perhaps the least offensive it has been shown to be responsible
for a large number of road accidents, particularly in combination
with alcohol. A recent entry on the scene is a new version of
cocaine, crack. Its increased speed of action produces an
exuberant high within seconds, and a severe depressive low
within minutes. Its addictive effect is the greatest of any illicit
drug. All these compounds lead to crime to obtain money for

further supplies, and to drug barons making high cash profits from trafficking and distribution. This causes an increase in organized crime of a particularly vicious kind.

In work stress and burnout these drugs are important because they become 'a way of life' which detracts from normal functioning at every level. Even weekend recreational use may lead to a bleak Monday morning, which will reveal not only the ravages of drugs and alcohol, but lead to absenteeism. Fortunately there are expertise and facilities to deal with these problems, but unfortunately the latter are totally inadequate. We must exert our pressure where appropriate politically to obtain more help for people who become addicted. Voluntary agencies try and fill the gap, and some individuals find that workers from these are more helpful in understanding the real problems than the professionals.

So it should be emphasized again that in a stressful situation the use of various substances that are at hand should be greatly curtailed. They only bring new problems, prevent us from seeing the situation as it is, how it may be resolved, or where we can seek help.

6

Women: The Conflict between
Home and Work

Women may have gained the vote and, at least in theory, share equal pay for equal work with men. But these battles have not been won without a struggle and the alteration in the role of women has not, as predicted, made their lot easier.

The wife of a Professor said to me over an excellent home-cooked dinner,

> My life as an emancipated woman is almost slavery, although I must admit I enjoy it. I look after the children, they are teenagers now, so they are a little help, but my husband still likes his shirts immaculate and he does not even attempt the ironing. Not only that, I have a full time job in the 'Save the Children Fund'; then I have to organize and prepare meals like this for my husband's friends and his colleagues at work. I am not regarded, however, as a success. Oh no, to be that I need also to have written a novel or two which received good notices in the best weeklies. We women really have to make our lives tough to succeed!

She went on to add that she often felt stressed but had a few ploys, a catnap, or a tapestry cushion cover to concentrate on for just a few minutes, that often did the trick. She admitted to not having many real friends to turn to. This showed up particularly when her mother died recently. Also her husband's constant absence over the summer at vacation schools or abroad at conferences did not help. There were problems with her son's GCSE exams, especially as he was not at all academic.

Certainly she was coping, though with what a complicated life! At least I thought to myself she was not trapped by boredom, which happens to many women who have resigned themselves to the house and the children and give up hope of a job. Even so it is not 9.0 to 5.0 as in an office but 7.0 am to 10.0 pm, when the children finally disappear upstairs to bed. Indeed a recent survey showed that at least 50 per cent of women have difficulty deciding between husband and family versus a job. Many say if they actually had a choice they would not know which way to jump!

Children and childlessness

One cannot deny that the contraceptive pill has played an important part in the liberation of women. They have freer choice, although as with every medicine there is the risk of side-effects, such as excessive blood clotting in various parts of the body. The chances of this are small and can be reduced by careful selection of people prescribed the pill. Other contraceptive methods all have some 'cost' to pay for gaining freedom: the 'morning after pill', more readily available abortion, and now sterilization. The man too can play his part: the vasectomy has its place and clearly this and sterilization need a different, more detailed approach, because for practical purposes they are irreversible.

There is also help for the childless. The newer techniques such as direct fertilized egg transplantation into the womb will clearly become more successful. Surrogate mothers form another, if controversial, group, but there are the beginnings of new hope for those who really want a family.

There is no doubt that the women's lib movement has come a long way since suffragettes chained themselves to the railings of Downing Street, but periodically there is a backlash. It is really not certain, as one male writer puts it, 'whether the pill or the car self-starter has been the most important in allowing freedom for women from endless domesticity!'

Swapping roles

Some families are successful at coping with both partners at work, though it is known to be a potent source of marital breakdown. When the children are younger they can and should both share the chores so that day-to-day tasks are organized with a minimum of friction. Today there is often total reversal when the man is unemployed. Many males do not relish this realm of duty but it is forced upon them.

Case history: Arthur

Arthur was a 28-year-old patient with epilepsy. He hated looking after the children, house cleaning and shopping while his wife was a successful advertising executive, and brought home the cash. His unemployment related to very frequent fits. Arthur came to the clinic with his wife and children. He sat there speechless, as she recounted his recent poor health. He was depressed, but antidepressants were clearly not appropriate for the type of illness. He was totally dependent on the poor control of his attacks. Fortunately a new antiepileptic compound became available and at once his fits were almost totally controlled. He got a portering post in a hospital near to his home. The children were now of school age, and his work was on a shift basis, so he could interleave with his wife's more standard office hours which in any case were fairly flexible.

The transformation was easy to see. Arthur became cheerful and talkative when he came for his checkups. Even though his job was ordinary he made the most of it because of his experience of illness and hospitals. He was able to talk and sympathize with the patients as he pushed them about the hospital. Sadly he died later from a series of fits for no apparent reason, but at least he had about ten years of a reasonably happy life.

Women at work

Being single has its own problems – and its own compensations. Freda, a 34-year-old executive, says she thrives on stress brought about by her 50 plus staff in a fashion clothes business. She has delegated her work so that she can do the usual 9.0 to 5.0 office hours, and not have to stay there until 10.0 or 11.0 at night, and she takes two good holidays a year. Illness of any kind she has treated by acupuncture. Yoga twice a week allows her to bounce back and thrive on whatever comes, whether business or personal. Ordinary shopping is done in a flash, but she likes to browse buying clothes, jewellery and cosmetics with care. Indeed, like more than half the women in one survey, shopping led to relaxation, as long as it did not include shopping for teenager's shoes or clothes which so often bring hassle! Those with families will be familiar with the feelings aroused on such necessary preterm shopping expeditions.

Women tend to choose a vocation so they can storm the bastions of the man's world as business executives, solicitors, architects and accountants. There is, however, a gap between the successful high flyer in such vocations and those trapped in poorly paid jobs, or now relegated to life at home with young families.

One way round this is to choose a career that can be developed with age – for example, nursing and medicine and related paramedical pursuits such as physiotherapy and radiography are particular groups that provide just this. There are many others. An established career can be taken up again after marriage when the children start school. At this stage nurses can specialize and become intensive care ward personnel or health visitors. Becoming a hospital consultant requires at least one higher qualification which will take, perhaps, four years to complete. This coupled with concentrated study in a recognized training post as well as commitments to routine work, busy wards and hectic outpatient departments are required. All these are often too difficult to combine with having and caring for a family. However, it can be done.

Women and health

One cannot deny that the physical and psychological changes accompanying menstruation, childbearing and the menopause have an effect on the work record. However, recognition that some bodily troubles require medical and surgical treatment where appropriate, as well as sympathetic handling, can reduce these effects to a minimum. Then of course there are the serious illnesses such as cervical cancer (tumours of the neck of the womb) and breast cancer, which take their toll, but fortunately even these are beginning to be recognized earlier, and a great variety of drug and other treatments are available, so the outlook is improving. On the negative side, smoking and alcohol consumption continues to increase in women. They are able to tolerate about half the amount of alcohol as men, and dependence on it leads to raised blood pressure, stomach ailments and liver disease. These are all on the increase, partly one suspects as women are more and more likely to be exposed to the same pressures of working life as men.

The menopause

Menopausal changes obviously affect different women in different ways. For some the impact is mainly physical, and for others it is psychological. Clearly there is a mixture of symptoms and feelings. Hormonal disturbance may lead to fatigue, nervousness, headaches, and migraine in some. Sleeplessness, dizziness, palpitations and depression may be present in variable amounts as seen in the case history below. Women are particularly liable to depression at the time of the menopause and after.

These symptoms and those of irritability and poor concentration all affect work, but all may be helped by hormone replacement therapy (HRT). Oestrogen, a female hormone manufactured in the body, is known to fall in association with the menopause. Regular administration is controversial, but if in your case you feel these symptoms are present and disturbing life in general, it is worth consulting the general practitioner, first to check that there is no serious underlying illness, and second to see if hormone replacement therapy is necessary and for how long.

Case history: Edna
Edna is a particular example. All had been well until her

husband died nine months before. Her mother had suffered from frequent serious bouts of depression, a psychiatric disorder known to be inherited. Edna had been a conscientious secretary in a glass manufacturing firm all her life. She was highly competent and it was only when her husband died – they had no children – that she began to ruminate on how life might have been with a family of her own. She came from a large family, and all her brothers and sisters had children. Edna felt left out. At first nobody at work noticed, then she started to have severe migraine. These had happened previously about once a year at most, but now missing days from the office were becoming such a recurrent feature that her boss suggested early retirement.

The effect was not at all as her boss had predicted; with no stress from work it was felt all would be well and perhaps Edna might take a part-time secretarial job. Instead she grew guilty and remorseful about her husband's death. She paced the floor wringing her hands, barely able to read, knit or watch television. Sleep and appetite were disturbed. Edna felt she was blundering through life, and talked of wishing to join her husband. However, psychiatric treatment in hospital was effective and in due course she did return to her old firm for a few years on a part-time basis.

The effect of the menopause in some women is a mainly psychological matter, a feeling of loss because the child-bearing era is over. This is often coupled with children leaving home so the family abode feels empty. However, this should not be considered as a time of loss but rather one of gain, bearing in mind the long life expectancy of women. In any case being a grandmother or grandfather is a pleasant chore! It is a moment when the future should be considered in detail, not as one of infirmity and invalidism, but as a period of renewed vigour and interest when the responsibility of raising children has subsided. Perhaps it is a time to seek different employment, or change to something more stimulating or remunerative. The menopause ushers in a new era of happy rewarding years which could outshine all those that have gone before.

Stability and sex

There is no doubt that a lasting stable relationship with a satisfactory sexual side is ideal as a background to happiness at work. The emotional maturity necessary implies not only self-confidence in oneself, but also a degree of objectivity and consistency, coupled with caring for others. This obviously spills over into every aspect of life, but employment, leisure, voluntary work and hobbies all add together to enhance society. Such relationships may or may not take children into consideration. Nowadays there are also those whose permanent relationship is with someone of the same sex.

However, whether the couple are married or not, or of the same sex, problems relate to varying dominance within the partnership which fluctuates from time to time. There has to be a degree of compromise, verbal duels followed by capitulation, but not always on the same side. However, if rearing of a family is contemplated there should be as much resolution of conflicts as possible early rather than later in the relationship.

The difficulties in marriage or other types of partnership may be many, and are often related to work. A happy and mutually satisfying sexual relationship is important in helping to cope with stress and heal life's hurts. As there is a multitude of books on sexual techniques to turn to I will not dwell on practical matters here. Suffice it to say that mutual trust and enjoyment almost inevitably wane with the passage of time, and such problems as frigidity and impotence appear. In fact more important is the basic lack of desire or interest for sexual activity, a problem that is often difficult to reverse. Complaints of fatigue, backache and pain on intercourse, compounded sometimes with poor performance resulting from excessive alcohol, can make the sexual side of the relationships a bore. The romantic notion of making love gives way to joyless sex. Don't let the fun go out of *your* sex life. As one author puts it, 'it needs to be frequent, fresh and flexible, and don't forget too it is a marvellous way of making up quarrels.'

Marriage

In spite of all these alterations in attitude, marriage remains a popular institution, although a recent survey has noted some changes. The age at which people marry has increased: in 1970 it was on average 27 years; in 1986 this had risen to 29 years. 'Living together' has become popular, especially in younger couples, though still only represents the choice of 10 per cent of women.

Alterations in the pattern of rearing a family have also occurred. Not unexpectedly there has been a reduction in the number of children born to women between the ages of 20 and 24, falling from fifteen per 1000, to nine per 1000 in ten years, with the opposite for women in their early 30s.

This same survey goes on to show changes in marriage break-up. We are all familiar with the poor success rate of teenage marriages as well as the increasing divorce rate over all ages. Traditionally, the dissolution of marriage has been on the male side. But now today women are just not prepared to tolerate a man that they do not want, so they call the tune in separation and divorce. In the early 1970s, perhaps 'for the sake of the children', only half of all divorces were started by the female partner. Now the figure has risen to three-quarters.

Competitiveness

A considerable problem in marriage or any kind of partnership is competitiveness, particularly when both are working in separate places. When employed together in the same establishment, there are both advantages and disadvantages. Indeed the streak of competitiveness is essential for success; and a degree of stress needs to be present to act as an energizer. Problems arise when the person is overambitious.

Take some simple examples: not content with one successful novel the author may want to write three; having won the Wimbledon tennis championship once the tennis player may want to be in the record books and be the first to win it nine times; not content with decorating the bathroom, sights become fixed on painting the whole house inside and out; sales figures doubled last year, they must treble this year, and so on. It is essential to keep within bounds, to avoid situations which lead to a marked increase in stress. But there is no ban on daydreaming if it is just that.

Keeping up with the Joneses

We are particularly prone to compete with neighbours: they went to Greece last year, so we shall go to Turkey; they have a Ford, we shall have a BMW. There are many other examples. Clothes and gadgets are both obvious. Have you been left behind without possessing a food processor or microwave, or a video recorder? Be thankful that you live in the United Kingdom rather than the United States where this kind of competition is rife. The pressure to join the fashion race impinges strongly on women, and may even lead to dislike of the very thought of returning to work to be confronted by the boastful woman who shares the office and is on a competitive wavelength all the time.

It would be trite to say that women are different from men in relation to work stress and burnout but that is just the case. The combination of coping with home and work in itself is stressful, yet many find being employed has a liberating effect, in contrast to the homemaker in the 'boredom' trap, a greater hazard perhaps than all the slave-driving bosses rolled into one.

7

Unemployment and Redundancy

Why, you may ask, should there be a chapter on unemployment and redundancy in a book on stress and job burnout? We need to understand the whole pattern of the available workforce. Strictly, 'work' embraces all sorts of occupations including, for example, that of a housewife who is not 'employed' as such, for she does not (directly) receive money proportionate to the tasks and hours involved. Work, according to the experts, means 'paid employment'. However, even this is not straightforward because moonlighting and labour exists within the 'black economy'.

Some examples of these might be carpet layers, and carpenters who also work evenings and weekends using their particular daytime skills and often being paid in cash. The telephone engineer, working by day with one of the national communication firms, who fixes a new telephone out of hours, not only gets a fee in his hand for this service, but also the difference between wholesale and retail price for the apparatus in cash. He has a tax advantage, but the price charged to the client is often cheaper than available in the ordinary marketplace so we all gain! (Work out who loses.)

There is also a question of married women at work. Many are part-time, others need to make arrangements for school holidays, or crêches to cope with preschool children. Part-time work in general causes many problems. These points have to be considered when assessing the totally unemployed.

Unemployment, job stress and burnout

Unemployment, or the threat of it, is a vital concern in relation to job stress and burnout. As we have seen already the instability in workplace – takeovers and the like – have great influence, also lack of markets for the goods produced, be it a question of price or quality. Anxiety about this in managers quickly transfers to the employee where there is soon talk of redundancy, often a polite way of saying 'sacking'. Difficulty over markets or loss of contracts can at times lead to both national and international unemployment. Even the threat of it sends shudders through the workforce, the unions and professional organizations.

Usually the most recently employed people are disposed of first: then older members of staff may be offered early retirement. Whether they accept or not depends on pension status, a matter of current concern, not least because of the growing ageing population in both the United Kingdom and in many other countries. The individual also has to consider whether there will be a golden handshake, a lump sum, to offset the sudden drop in regular income.

This is not all. Surveys of the unemployed have shown that their health is poor as a group, even immediately after they lose their jobs, compared with the employed. Nearly 20 per cent in a Department of Health and Social Security study said that they had a medical problem; research into this continued until the end of the year after they became unemployed. Many remained in poor health throughout that time.

In my experience, patients who are disabled in some way may not only find a job difficult to get, but at times of high unemployment are the first to be made redundant. Statistics show that in fact they try hardest not to take time off work for illness, and their absenteeism rate may often be *lower* than their more fortunate non-disabled colleagues.

Who are the unemployed?

Those in work often tend to belittle the unemployed. This is quite unfair and out of line with known facts from a number of points of view. Dramatic reports of suicide in teenagers and others unable to get jobs or find another one, have underlined the plight of many. The matter is complicated by the 'depressed' areas that occur in the United Kingdom, the United States and Australia as well as many other countries.

The jobless are overrepresented in the young and the old,

single men, those with large families, the unhealthy, disabled, socially disadvantaged and ethnic minorities. Unemployment is associated with poverty and poor housing, and there is a strong link between this and deterioration in both physical and psychological health. The professionals who study population trends divide unemployment for their purposes into three main groups; fractional, structural, and cyclical.

Fractional This consists of those who are simply out of work between jobs. To give some example of the size of this group, nine million jobs change hands in the United Kingdom within a year, so obviously this figures in the jobless statistics.

Structural This arises from the mismatch of work available and the skills of the unemployed. The decline in heavy industry and coalmining where traditionally many unskilled jobs were available has left a pool of men who need retraining before new employment can be found. With the rapid growth of high technology, there are vacancies in electronics and electrical industries – an interesting field where women play a major role in providing what firms require.

The mismatch problem must also be considered in relation to the young. School-leavers need to be directed towards areas where there are opportunities, otherwise they may be unable to find jobs. It is essential that they obtain examinations at the end of their school careers, even if they do not intend at that stage to go on to college or university. These will provide opportunities in the future, bearing in mind (as we shall see in Chapter 10) that much more rapid changes are expected in the pattern of work as we approach the end of this century and the beginning of the next. Projection of the requirements of the future is essential and comes within the governmental and political sway.

Cyclical This is not unrelated to the two groups above, but is essentially economic. Fall off in industrial production and recession is beyond the control of employers, and not limited to particular trades. It is a very important concern at the moment, as most developed countries are suffering unemployment. Here political forces must be used to reverse the trend, and obviously large appropriate training programmes are needed to counteract this and structural unemployment.

The cyclical type of unemployment can be seen in miniature each year, with the seasonal changes of spring and summer. For example, when the weather improves there is an increase in employment of building and construction workers, those in the holiday trades, hotel catering, and travel industries. Seasonal unemployment clouds the statistics, so the old phrase 'seasonally adjusted figures still show an upward trend' is the kind of thing we see with government-published figures.

Case history: Clive

Clive, a jeweller in his late 40s, though well trained in his youth had worked for one firm all his life, a family business with two shops. The boss died and his son decided to sell up and realize the assets. All the staff were made redundant, and Clive could not find a similar job. He totally lost interest in work, but was persuaded to go on a government training scheme, and later a community project. However, neither led to job prospects or a positive outlook when they ended. He now languishes at home six years on with little hope for the future, bored and helpless. Clive is in the sad band of the permanently unemployed, who represent a small proportion of the total monthly figures. He is no longer even interested enough to look for work.

The myths of unemployment

The majority of people out of work desperately want a job and regard joblessness as a bad thing. In one survey only 8 per cent were not actively looking for work, mainly due to age. It is also not true that the unemployed are often better off out of work. Joblessness causes not only poverty, but boredom, as money is required for many leisure pursuits. Fortunately, for this reason many local authorities provide cheap bus passes, and places of entertainment allow the workless to have the same rates as senior citizens.

It is not surprising that many jobless turn to excessive drinking which leads to financial, mental and moral decline. Though the experts have not found a clear association, the presence of high unemployment must be deprecated in any caring society.

When recession occurs on a worldwide scale it is not just the individual who suffers, it is the poor underdeveloped countries as a whole. Hence the enormity of the current problems of the third world with its debts to richer nations. So far resolving this has only proved possible on a limited scale, in spite of the many meetings of financial experts.

What does unemployment tell us about work?

It is interesting how much we learn about work when we think about unemployment. First of all, not having a regular job has a much greater effect than loss of pay alone. There is no pattern to the day, no particular time to get up, to have a tea or lunch break, or pint on the way home. There is also a loss of friends, and contacts that take one out of the family circle. Tensions in the home are exaggerated because the former breadwinner is there for much of the day. This, coupled with the loss of belonging to anything outside or having no purpose or sense of achievement, leads inevitably to irritability, tiredness and total loss of interest. In certain towns the presence of streets and streets of unemployed people affects the shops, pubs and clubs, and depression spreads beyond the immediate vicinity. This atmosphere does not stimulate those who live there to go out and find another job.

8

Early Retirement, Disability and Ill-health

Early retirement

The prospect for a man or woman in their early 50s obtaining employment is bleak. Their particular niche in the factory or office has perhaps been lost because of a takeover and subsequent reorganization. Or there may be change in work practices due to automation and the use of computers. Retraining would seem to be the answer, but often it is not feasible, partly because the employee is set in his or her ways, or the employer offers no facilities, so in these circumstances early retirement seems an easy option. Some of my patients are in this situation; one particular one springs to mind.

Case history: Elsie

Elsie is in her mid-50s, the age group where many of the most poignant stories are found: business executives rejected by the firm who took over, steel workers left high and dry by reorganization and closures to increase profitability, and even the professional footballer, a mere 35 years old, left on the scrap heap.

Elsie worked for a long-established manufacturer of car components. In the case of such organizations the plant and process can become out-of-date, with an equally ageing management. Senior executives failed to appreciate that the continuing profitability of their shares on the Stock Exchange hid a dismal situation. Clearly some of the profits must always be reserved for replacement of the plant but this had not been done for years. A new Australian whizzkid was brought in. The office was just one of the areas in which he concentrated. Gone were the creaky typewriters, and VDUs, word proces-

59

sors, and the latest computer facilities for billing and stock control were introduced. Elsie tried, hanging on grimly for a couple of years, to smooth the rough ride of transition from manual to automated systems. Her migraine got the better of her in the midst of the flashing screens and the endless clatter of printers. She took early retirement and has been moderately happy ever since.

Stress and physical ill-health

Migraine is an example of a condition that can be made worse by stress in some sufferers. In others the attacks are probably triggered by irregular food, certain phases of the menstrual cycle, or without any particular cause. Just how the attacks, due to sudden narrowing of the blood vessels in the brain coverings as well as the scalp muscles, are triggered, is uncertain. However, as in other physical illnesses, there is a clear association with tension in both work and private life. Conditions as different as asthma, backache, colitis, and psoriasis are examples of stress-related disorders, as are stomach ulcers. Bob's story, which follows, indicates how stress may lead to physical illness.

Case history: Bob

Bob, a 50-year-old long-distance lorry driver, is an example of someone who apparently took stress in his stride but eventually developed a distinct physical illness. He had been driving a big truck, and more recently a juggernaut, for more than 30 years, going to more and more remote parts of Europe and away from home often for many days at a time. He enjoyed the work, he felt in command of his own particular world. He preferred to drive for many hours at a stretch although more recently with the introduction of a tachometer this was no longer possible. In any case the companies for whom he had worked before did not approve of his work pattern. He was essentially a freelance driver, working as much as anything for his own satisfaction. The combination of driving stress, which he did not recognize, irregular sleep due to long stints at the wheel, and intermittent heavy meals caused him to develop stomach pains on and off during the 24 hours while driving.

The cause of the trouble was quickly demonstrated on special x-ray as a stomach ulcer, due to long-continued unrecognized stress. In Bob's case this was the end of his driving career. It completely changed his family's life and led to considerable tension. He and his wife had grown apart, and being home every night in close contact with her only increased the tension in a not particularly happy marriage. They just continued to muddle through and Bob, a previously happy person, completely changed. There was no real solution.

The link between stress and illness is obviously complicated, though we can now see part of the pattern. Ill-health leads increasingly to time off work; this leads to concern at the workplace where the likely outcome is often redundancy.

Non-employment in the form of early retirement can sometimes have a marked effect. Elsie was happy in her retirement. However, illness results in both loss of earnings and increased family strain. The situation may worsen to such an extent that the individual becomes unemployable.

Disability and employment

Another group needs here at least a passing mention: the disabled. Sometimes it can be overwhelming as in the case of Maria, a tragic example leading to employment difficulty. Here is her sad story that appeared in the press worldwide.

Case history: Maria

Maria, an American, has been called the 'elephant woman' because of her severe disfigurement. She had a lopsided face and a trunk-like nose with cleft palate. Hearing and seeing were difficult because the whole of the right side of her face was malformed and led to a completely twisted appearance. The deformity was so bad that passengers on buses she

61

boarded often got off at the next stop! In spite of over 100 operations and a degree in psychology she could not get a job. She could cope with her face, but she was not able to get employment. Potential bosses would say that she was just too ugly to work even in the backroom away from the public gaze. The 'elephant man' solved his problem by becoming almost a hermit, hidden away permanently from view in a small basement room of the London Hospital, but Maria was different; she wanted to live life and meet people. She pounded pavements for jobs, and when she died (after a major and risky operation) her mother found her room full of rejection letters.

Maria's case, of course, was extreme. Not all disabilities, fortunately, are quite so overwhelming and they need to be considered under various headings. There is, like Maria's, a type of deformity which of whatever severity is unchanging, for example, the wasted, twisted weak limbs after infantile paralysis, or following a serious road accident. Then there are progressive, degenerative disorders, usually in the older age group, some carrying with them serious memory loss and consequent problems for day-to-day living. These occur in various forms of dementia, affecting the brain, an example being Alzheimer's disease. Sometimes the muscles and nerves degenerate for no known reason, and the person becomes progressively more incapacitated over a period of months or years, eventually relegated to a wheelchair. The film actor, David Niven, had one such disorder, known as 'motor neurone disease'.

Multiple sclerosis affects both brain and nerves; though the final results are similar to those of motor neurone disease, it is different in various respects. First of all, and most tragically, it may affect teenagers or those in their early 20s. Multiple sclerosis is not generally a slowly progressive disorder, at least in early years. It often starts with a sudden attack of blindness in one eye, or weakness of an arm or leg. In a few weeks the sight returns almost completely as does the power of the limbs. Attacks recur, scattered over many years, hence the name disseminated, but tend to leave scars in the nervous tissue so a progressive decline is often, but not always, the outcome. Again the cause of the disorder is unclear, but various forms of treatment can be helpful for individual attacks if not the overall disorder.

Another disability, intermittent and usually with no progressive decline, is epilepsy. The fits themselves are frightening for the patient, the parent and the workmates but are not usually in themselves very serious. Death from an attack is extremely rare, but injuries may sometimes result from the associated falls. Usually non-sedative drugs control the attacks, so they occur perhaps in bed at night once or twice a year.

Patients with epilepsy also have considerable difficulty in obtaining employment, although each firm or organization above a certain size has by law to employ a small percentage of disabled people. They register at the job centre and in theory have job priority. Workers in this category can be very useful members of the workforce, and frequently indicate to other employees how an individual can overcome problems, with little absenteeism or time off work from ill-health.

One major problem for the disabled is mobility. Fortunately there is increasing provision in schools and workplaces, as well as leisure facilities, for wheelchairs, but many disabled have problems in car use: finding a parking place, for example, near the office, as well as the cost and upkeep of the vehicle. There is also the question of eligibility for a driving licence. Strict rules apply particularly to epileptics, so that the driving licence cannot be issued if an attack has occurred within two years. There are also clearcut regulations for other disabilities that obviously affect work and leisure activities, and impair the quality of life for the sufferer.

It can now be appreciated that stress at work can lead to physical change in the individual; ill-health and unemployment may follow. Job stress needs to be attacked, as has been seen, from many angles. In Chapter 9 we shall consider what further steps can be taken if the simple measures of 'first aid' suggested in Chapter 4 have not brought relief.

9

Seek Help and Share
the Problem

The key to overcoming job stress and burnout is to seek help and
this means sharing the problems. If they have become too
overwhelming and the action suggested in Chapter 4 has not
been of any avail, look at Table 6, an itemized checklist of the
many and various sources of help that are available; you may
gain some confidence from the contents.

Table 6   Pursuing help (see also Tables 4 and 5)

- Have you exhausted the support that partner, friend and
  family can give?
- What about colleagues at work?
- Is there any other professional assistance you need?
- Do you require medical help?
- Is psychiatric advice or counselling needed?
- Can the personnel department at work offer any help?
- Is it worth trying relaxation, yoga, acupuncture or other
  forms of alternative medicine?
- Have all the above failed? Try relocation, early retirement,
  with or without a golden handshake – or just quit

Partner, family and friends

You may already have tried to resolve matters by sharing with
those close to you. The question here is have you been quite
frank as to the serious nature of the job stress and burnout. Try
not to ruminate on the same ideas talking about them repeatedly
in the same way. This becomes a bore and I really mean a bore; it
will not help you, and others will be less inclined to give
appropriate advice.

Make some notes for yourself as to the crucial issues and attempt to add to these notes from time to time. Keeping a diary can also be helpful. If there is any suggestion that you could resort to legal action due to the undue strain and stress that is placed on you by a firm or organization, then make detailed notes with dates: who you saw and what happened must be recorded carefully to present to your legal advisors.

Colleagues at work

Colleagues at work may be able to offer specific help because they can also indicate if your problems are in true perspective, or whether your mind is clouded and your view of what is happening in the work situation is quite 'off the mark'. In any case they may be able to help resolve some of the difficulties with other colleagues. A few discreet words in various appropriate quarters can be of great help without compromising your own position.

Professional advice

Next you must decide whether to seek professional advice. Have you a good relationship with a priest, or a family medical practitioner? If in financial difficulties, can you consult a bank manager or accountant (see Chapter 4). They may understand that the points you raise have a much wider implication and be able to suggest various sources of help. In this way you have mobilized many and various ideas as well as determining which people will support you, so that a major assault can be mounted on the difficulties.

Medical help

One person you should consider contacting early on is your family doctor. Even if you do not know him or her well, or feel that there is any affinity, it is an essential move. In any case, in the type of group practice found nowadays, individual doctors tend to have a particular interest; when they encounter more complex problems they set aside time outside the rushed surgery hours to consider difficult matters in depth. You should raise any specific health problems with the doctor if you are worried. These can often be easier dealt with than other more complex issues, by an examination, blood test, checking blood pressure and so on. Normal findings in relation to all these will help to set your mind at rest, at least on the practical matters.

Questions about smoking, alcohol intake, caffeine and tranquillizers were dealt with in Chapter 5; all these may be increasing rather than decreasing tension symptoms.

Psychiatric help

Problems at work can lead to depressive ideas which may vary from a feeling of utter failure, to guilt, anger and severe irritability. Depression, then, is not just a reaction to the problem but has reached the stage where it is a true illness, particularly when suicidal ideas are dominant in the mind. The general practitioner may feel that this and other problems such as dependence on alcohol require psychiatric treatment. The psychiatrist, or even the general practitioner, may suggest help through psychotherapy – obviously this will depend on what is available locally. Essentially this consists of a more detailed look at the pattern of life, emotions and motives that may be at the heart of the problems.

Counselling

Basically what may be required is to talk things over, not in the usual way, casually letting the conversation drift, but with someone totally unconnected with family or work who is trained to direct thoughts into particular problem areas. He or she will attempt to unravel complex problems like yours which may have arisen over many years. If this proves to be the case then psychotherapy may be required to resolve wide-ranging psychological problems – personal, marital and sexual – as well as in the work field. Counselling is a little different, as it tends to concentrate on more specific problems such as difficulties at work.

Some particularly tough jobs present special problems: the fireman who was so devastated by a horrific road accident that he needed professional help to unravel his tangled emotions; the social worker concerned with the abuse of children, physical and sexual, who may feel under great pressure because of the present concerns with misjudgements reported widely in the media.

In many professions there is a distinct way of progressing through the various stages. This has already been mentioned in relation to women doctors and others. Those who choose a vocation may find that their ideas of simply caring for the sick, or looking after abandoned children, are no longer quite as straightforward as they had first seemed. They need help and advice either to continue in their chosen field or completely to change their life pattern and take a new direction, perhaps abroad or in industry rather than in the National Health Service.

Then there is the bank clerk who was persuaded by his parents that this type of employment offers a safe, secure job for life. However, he found the work utterly boring. Within a few months, stress had developed, and absenteeism and minor physical illness repeatedly caused time off work. He should perhaps have sought professional help; instead he 'ran away' and joined the Navy.

A TV producer working in a large busy station living on her nerves was excited by the work but agonized over whether, for example, a particular show might overrun, had the correct emphasis or the appropriate narrator. Counselling eased the immediate work problem, but in the event it was a university public relations job rather than a hectic television career that allowed her talents to flow naturally and offered her more rewarding opportunities than her initial chosen career.

So sometimes leaving a job or taking a new direction will be the way of not only reducing stress but also allowing the natural abilities to be used to the full. This we shall consider later in this chapter.

Personnel department

Let us now return to the sort of help that may be possible within the work situation itself. You will almost certainly have spoken to your immediate superior, perhaps with little helpful response. Follow this up by arranging an interview with someone more senior in the office, firm or organization, who is more remote from everyday problems. Whatever has gone before, it is important to inform your immediate manager or supervisor of your plan of action. But tread carefully unless you feel that any grievance is really justified. You may be caught in crossfire which is not necessarily advantageous. A union representative or the personnel department staff may be a better source of help than a face-to-face confrontation. Here is an example.

Case history: Betty

Betty works in a hospital department responsible for providing sterilized instruments for the wards and operating theatres. A new young departmental manager was brought in to streamline the facilities, no doubt with ideas of saving money and better results in productivity terms. After a 'honeymoon period' when all the employees in the workplace considered him an improvement on the previous boss he became more forthright in his views. He asked Betty to help train a new member of staff. Though not a supervisor, Betty was happy to 'show her the ropes', but her workmates said, 'If you help to train that new girl we will report you to the union'. Betty was very depressed about this. Fortunately the hospital had trained people in both personnel department and the occupational health sections who could help, and the problem was resolved, but not before a lot of heartache.

Relieving stress through alternative medicine

Taking into account all the various work-related problems that have been brought to the fore recently, particularly in the United States, great emphasis has been placed on prevention programmes. Short lectures in the lunch break to encourage 'wellness', healthier diets, exercise, and smoking reduction have all been topics, as well as methods for better time management. Teaching workers to take their jobs less seriously is one way – 'humour programmes' help employees to unwind. Stress consultants help workers to take difficulties in their stride.

Microdots

Coupled with these approaches there are more technical innovations such as the use of 'microdots', small temperature-sensitive adhesive devices that workers can attach to their hands. When the person is tense the blood flow is reduced and this shows by lowering the skin temperature, as recorded by the disc. Another sign of stress is a pounding heart, a rapid pulse and a rising blood pressure which can be found on examination by a doctor. In these days of rapidly advancing technology, all these bodily responses can be recorded using a cassette, which can be examined later to track increases in, for example, the pulse rate. Some such devices have a button to press that marks the tape and acts as event-marker, so that the person can indicate what they were doing at a particular time when they felt stressed.

Biofeedback

Here a device produces an audible sound that corresponds directly to what is happening, for example, in the blood circulation. Alternatively, with almost invisible small discs attached to the scalp by glue or sticky tape a small signal can be received from the brain and recorded by a miniature apparatus attached to the waist. This can, for example, indicate whether alpha rhythm, the brain activity that corresponds to relaxation, is present or not. Learning to increase this type of signal from the attached electrodes enhances relaxation and has been used in people with high blood pressure to allow them to control the level without having to take tablets.

Relaxation: imaging and yoga

Relaxation we can do ourselves at home or even at work in

rest periods. In the simplest form the person learns to take a few really deep breaths slowly, and put the mind in neutral there and then if something is producing stress. This can be done almost anywhere. Others prefer to conjure up a mental picture which causes warmth. This technique, called *imaging*, may for some prove a very effective way of relaxing.

A more detailed full-scale relaxation technique is given by Dr Vernon Coleman in *Overcoming Stress* (1988). He describes a 20-point plan to relax the body. It takes a little time to learn, but when mastered a quarter of an hour in a darkened room is all that is required, repeated daily to give maximum results. The principle is simple: you first create tension by contracting different muscles and then relaxing them. So one starts, for example, with the left hand, clenching it so tightly that the knuckles go white, then unfold the fist and feel the muscles relax. This pattern is repeated with the legs, stomach etc, and the result can be most effective.

Others prefer *yoga* techniques or a purely mental approach with various forms of *meditation*. Some of these measures are readily available at little cost. Others are run by commercial enterprises where help may come expensively, by courses, personal advice and by a device such as the biofeedback apparatus mentioned above. These adjuncts may not all be absolutely necessary.

To quit or not

Let us consider what to do if all the lines of approach suggested have been to no avail, allowing time for any approach to have an effect. However, if matters are not improving, or actually getting worse, there is no doubt that serious consideration should be given to a few other alternatives.

If the problem has arisen from undue promotion, then reverting to a previous level of work which proved satisfactory though less well paid may be the best approach.

If the company, firm or organization is a big one and your

performance has been limited because of local difficulties in a particular office or branch, then ask for a transfer, say from a busy London office to a quieter country town branch. Banks or large stores are often quite helpful in these difficult cases. Should this not be possible from either you or your employer's point of view, then you must consider leaving. Here carefully weighing the pros and cons is important, especially financially. You may be able to get a lump sum – a golden handshake – as well as a pension. Such money will tide you over until you find another job, if you are not seeking early retirement. This alternative is often suggested by the employer, perhaps on health grounds, if stress has become so much of a problem as to lead to definite illness. In these cases the settlements are often quite generous even well before the ordinary retiring age. There is always difficulty as to how this money should be invested, and professional help must be sought. Sometimes it gives financial security that the individual has never had before.

Starting work on one's own account, or even a small business venture, can be a possibility, since the available money can be used as starting capital. There are many striking examples of successful ventures, following from redundancy or forced early retirement. A woman in her mid-40s started a secretarial firm to service a new small business section in her expanding home town. A man in his early 50s found no new employment after months of searching; a college course seemed to be the answer. After the course he decided to turn his lifelong interest in old furniture from a hobby into a small business, renovating antiques.

In both examples very hard work was needed but great satisfaction resulted, and coupled with being in charge of their own lives and the enhanced financial reward this was ample compensation for the increased effort.

To reduce stress, we must look at all likely sources of help. Even if in the end one has to walk away from a particular situation the aim must be, as one expert put it, 'to combine common sense with counselling, so that we can learn to fight back when confronted with stress in a new post'.

Even greater changes are to be expected in the future, and these are dealt with in Chapter 10.

10

The Future of Work

Job stress and burnout were not topics that those writing about work 20 years ago (Scott, 1970) ever considered in detail. What will the next 20 years bring? Some obvious trends will continue, but there are also new quite unexpected directions that work will take, which we probably do not appreciate at the present time. Let us now examine some of the alterations already apparent.

Changing patterns at work

Computers

The use of computers has changed our lives; and we must appreciate that they are here to stay. This has meant that visual display units (VDUs) are now installed in many workplaces, and distant terminals via ordinary telephone lines are possible, so that some people can carry out their jobs comfortably at home rather than in a communal office. There are also small, yet powerful portable computers that allow even greater flexibility of routine work.

Flexitime

Another, unrelated, trend has been flexitime, originally used primarily to help women. The idea was to allow not only adjustments in the actual hours at work, but to stagger travelling times, reducing rush hour traffic and commuter train crushes.

Nowadays flexibility has expanded to such arrangements as job-sharing, teleworking and networking, all excellent schemes aimed at married women who want to combine career with child care. These ideas should be extended widely, so as to be of use to men as well as women. However, a difference remains. Present figures show that more than 40 per cent of the female workforce are part-time, the majority married, but only about 3 per cent of men have part-time status.

Flexible working hours have had great advantages that are not seen immediately. Using this technique employees can undertake further or higher education, particularly important as work opportunities are likely to come thick and fast for those who have skills and know how to develop as well as to use new technological advances. By staggering working hours we can plan and aim towards a rewarding retirement, develop skills to help the less fortunate, become more involved in active sport and leisure activities. Opportunities can also be opened up for the physically and mentally handicapped, who are often unable to take up full-time employment.

Freelancing

'I work at home' is a phrase now frequently heard much more than previously. There has always been 'home work' in various industries like the clothing trade, centred in such places as the East End of London. It is based on numerous small businesses, notorious for paying very small wages and providing the minimum of facilities for the work force. The term 'sweat shop', if not appropriate now, certainly has been so in the past.

The other trend has been in the growth of small business ventures often based on using the phone – for example, organizing driving lessons or providing information of various sorts. Writers and artists have always worked at home and this is now coupled with an increase in 'cottage industries' such as pottery, weaving and furniture-making. A tendency in this field is towards give-away copies of publications on the street or through the letterbox. These are intended to stimulate the growth of specialized sections of trade, often based on a particular area of a big city, and aimed at the more affluent groups of society.

In the home itself we are about to see radical change. About 20 years from now automation of the kitchen and housework by use of robots or simple devices, like sophisticated timers, will greatly assist all of us. These changes will give us more flexible use of our time and energy so that it may be developed for leisure.

The future in the workplace

Awareness of psychological problems at work has clearly increased in the last ten years, although to some extent it is only a change in emphasis. Concern about increasing job satisfaction has now altered with concentration on methods for reducing job stress, including stress management programmes and after-work aerobics. Often management can be almost totally devoted to cost-cutting, which will mean redundancy and early retirement, not a good climate for boosting the morale of the employees. The ideal manager of the future, if one can find him, should not be devoted entirely to cost-consciousness but more importantly to communication with employees involving them with creative ventures.

Often the new manager aims at increasing profitability so the workforce must be, to use the current jargon, 'downsized'; this means, in other words, more job losses. It seems therefore that unemployment in developed countries will not go away readily. One solution may be to work shorter hours and to take more leisure, so that people will be employed for a decreased working week, rather than lose their jobs.

Looking back we can appreciate that there is already a tendency to a reduction of the working week, but this and consequent alteration in employment will not eliminate unemployment. Other countries in Europe and elsewhere have similar difficulties.

Retraining

Emphasis on retraining is necessary, and it is particularly important that school-leavers appreciate that they can expect to change jobs, even careers, several times in their working life. Often retraining will become commonplace and hopefully readily accepted. Such a situation was quite unthinkable in the past, and in my case ten years were devoted to training as a specialist in medical practice, linked with the 20 following years practising within that sphere. This cannot be expected in the future. However, even my career has had a change in direction and emphasis, with increasing technology bringing about, for example, computer-assisted brain and body scanning techniques.

Information technology

With the growth in complexity of business it is important that information is available to all levels of management, but particularly in the middle ranks so that rational decisions can be taken. Information Technology (IT for short) is already being used widely in many areas of work. Money-saving decisions are often feasible, but more important the best deployment of capital available to the company or organization can be made. This has been applied in as diverse areas as the travel industry and hospital patient care, based on computerized equipment, both hardware and software.

A most striking use of IT has been in the travel industry where the Thomson holiday travel group were able, using a new IT reservation system, to increase their share in the ruthless competitive market. In two years the number of customers rose from 1.8 to three million, a staggering 67 per cent rise. Clearly the provision of instant IT systems for assessing all areas of working life and indeed leisure, not just to expand but operate with greater efficiency, is already of importance and will become increasingly so. It is a field in which thorough training is absolutely essential.

The cost of advance

Cheaper energy is important for all industries, but savings are often made at the cost of increased risk to human life. Coal-mining has been relatively cheap, but miners suffer danger and illness. Electricity based on nuclear power has not been obtained without considerable cost – the environmental effects of Chernobyl are incalculable.

The continuing human toll due to stress at work can be alleviated. One example is a secretary, often the victim of the boss, becoming the 'office wife'. One work expert put the view that the boss–servant relationship should be replaced by a partnership, with the focus on 'getting the job done and not on the relative status of those involved'. This will lead to changes in the secretary's role. However, changes in the speed of storing and retrieving information at the touch of a button, though enhancing personal work, may increase the problems of stress.

In these changing times it is essential to be alerted to all possible alterations, not only in technology and in the business world in general, but also how we manage ourselves at home. Whatever our situation, can we make use of our time in a satisfying manner? We must be aware that stress is now a way of life and can get seriously out of hand; it needs to be kept constantly under review and control. Emphasis on prevention is essential. This is the subject of Chapter 11.

11

Facing the Future with Confidence

When tensions and stresses have been reduced and burnout somehow conquered, we must not revert to our old ways that led to the problems. These may be revealed more as staleness, boredom and disinterestedness than tension. Problems at work unfortunately tend to recur, so we need to be vigilant always, to make sure that our life is constantly being renewed.

Mid-life crisis

Though burnout may occur at any age it is also part of the so-called 'mid-life crisis', especially as middle age tends to be a time when the person has, because of the current job structure, been in the same work situation for many years. But middle age can be, and should be, a time of opportunity. The routines of the job are well known and can easily be discharged. This should leave energy and often time to branch out. Indeed changes and opportunities may arise without effort. These include advice directly to do with the job, asked personally or in committees, or by the union or professional organizations or even by various political parties and pressure groups. There is a possibility of attending conferences and seminars, a chance to give lectures or write up some of the experience gained. Many other directions may be revealed. These may involve a change in a set pattern of work – they must be taken and not rejected out of hand.

Such changes will refresh, and new ideas will feed back into the ordinary work situation and revitalize it. Further, new social contacts may again lead to a change in attitude and perhaps the re-evaluations and realization that one's own work is not so mundane as it has seemed to be. We often forget that others have similar problems.

Reaching a particular birthday or anniversary is like the New

Year, a time for reflection, but the mere passage of time is relative. The 40th, 50th and 60th birthdays are all greeted with dismay. We resort to such phrases as 'life begins at 40' to cover up. We joke about policemen getting younger, or in my case I now turn to the obituaries rather than the job appointments in the *British Medical Journal*!

At all ages we must try to accomplish something – to do with not just work but home, hobbies and friends – and it should change with each decade. It is a good idea to concentrate on one particular area of life outside the work situation which is of special interest, be it the Society for the Protection of Birds, the problems of battered wives, learning Spanish or perfecting forgotten piano techniques. Dr Brice Pitt (1980) reviews all the middle age-related problems and presents positive and comforting views for those who are within this life band. He sees it as 'the time we may find new experiences and a new perspective so that we not only enjoy a full life but make sense of it'.

This sentiment should apply equally to all ages. Those in their teens need to be made aware of the sort of experience that life has ahead so they can best prepare for it. The perspectives offered by their secondary school at the age of eleven has now disappeared and the adult world must be embraced.

It is often difficult for both child and parent to make a career decision at school leaving time. Nowadays, if a decision cannot be made job experience is probably the answer rather than a hasty and regretted choice which leads to stress, and a wide range of physical symptoms that cause absence from work.

Body or mind?

It may be difficult for medical people to decide whether what the patient suffers from is actual physical disease – or is it 'all in the mind'? This particular dilemma has been crystallized in the 1980s by a disease characterized by extreme tiredness and muscle aching which now goes under a variety of different names from 'myalgic encephalomyelitis' (ME for short) to 'yuppie flu' (see below).

The cause of absence from work on medical grounds has always been a subject of controversy, since many of the reasons put forward, like flu, backache and migraine, do not have any definite signs that can be established by a doctor's examination. So from the point of view of the employer, the medical practitioner, and statisticians who concoct figures about absence from work and their causes, they are somewhat suspect. Nevertheless, in terms of numbers they are an important cause of absenteeism.

It is now being appreciated that many such disorders are provoked by stress at work indicating a body/mind interaction. Joining the diagnostic headings is myalgic encephalomyelitis. It remains a mystery, in spite of a great deal of research, particularly as it may affect groups of people in almost epidemic proportions. This has led psychiatrists to believe that it is an example of mass hysteria, while virologists hold the view that this disorder (like, for example, glandular fever) is due to an infection. They believe that many ME sufferers are being labelled wrongly as having a psychological disorder. Others hold the view that sufferers have a mixture of medical and mental symptoms, and point to the fact that many have very high aims which they may not be able to fulfil to their own satisfaction.

The reader may ask, 'Who has not suffered at some stage of their lives from tiredness and exhaustion?' ME sufferers have a cluster of different symptoms – it is not a mere tiredness but a 'devastating' weakness, not to mention a variety of features such as tingling in the hands and feet, slurring of speech, headache, feelings of sickness and bowel upsets, difficulty in focusing, disturbance of sleep, concentration and memory – these make it clearly an overwhelming disorder. Research into the disease swings from the entirely psychological to the entirely pathological, and we must wait for a final statement – but certainly some of these symptoms are well recognized as part of job stress. Prevention, as well as combatting, of this disorder will require a complex combination of talents, not least an appreciation of one's own ability and limitations.

Know yourself

A person is an infinite combination of hopes and ambitions, successes and failures which need to be seen and accepted. So that work can be a happy part of life there must be contentment in other areas, at home and beyond. If work allows little of interest, attention must be directed elsewhere. Devoting energy to enthralling hobbies, voluntary work or local politics can be the answer; they are a good investment for satisfaction. When there is serious work stress it is the spouse or partner, family and friends who lose.

Case history: Peter

Take Peter, a psychologist, who decided to take time out of employment to study for a PhD. He was married, he thought happily, with a young daughter. He worked very hard on his research and did not have a lot of money, but was contented that the prospect of a higher degree would place him potentially in a much more elevated salary bracket at the end of his studies. His wife returned to part-time work as a teacher. He did a lot for his daughter, like bathing her, taking her on outings to the park, the zoo or the fair. They did paintings together and he read her bedtime stories. As the academic career was causing a lot of tension, the time he spent with his daughter was an oasis of pleasure and peace, a time to recharge his energy and devote it to his research. But sadly in Peter's case his wife left him for another man and took their daughter with her.

Was Peter's decision to do a higher degree incorrect, or was his marriage going to break up anyway? We do not know; such major changes of course can be a success, but they need careful consideration and the co-operation of both partners. The family should be able to afford a means of adding something to the communal life, but it is important not to lose a sense of balance because otherwise work or home life may go radically wrong.

Maintain physical and mental strength

Whatever the psychological traumas and decisions it is essential to maintain physical fitness with a good diet, exercise and little or no tobacco and alcohol. Ample sleep and rest, weekend breaks and holidays are all part of keeping a state of equilibrium. Lists of chores essential both at home and work are useful, so keeping up to date with all these necessary everyday items can prevent worry and more serious problems from arising.

Cope with frustration: if the gas bill seems to be too high, a letter or a phone call should be made; if a difficulty arises with a colleague at work, give it attention as soon as possible.

Do not let anger build up. Deal with minor problems at the time, rather than letting them get out of hand. Protests should be honest and well-intentioned and this will dissipate tension. Realize that reducing stress, by whatever means, is worthwhile. If you have had real problems in the past they may recur; be alert to this possibility.

Bear in mind then that difficulties vary with age and circumstances, but the general approach outlined in this book should, I hope, be helpful.

Further Reading

Coleman, Vernon (1988) *Overcoming Stress*, Sheldon
Pitt, Brice (1980) *Midlife Crisis*, Sheldon
Scott, Donald (1970) *The Psychology of Work*, Duckworth
Redundancy, *Which* (August 1988) Consumer Association
  Ltd, Hertford
Tyrer, Peter (1980) *Stress*, Sheldon

Index

INDEX